Creating America

A History of the United States

**Beginnings
through
Reconstruction**

McDougal Littell

Evanston, Illinois • Boston • Dallas

Acknowledgments

Grove/Atlantic: Excerpt.from *Citizen Tom Paine* by Howard Fast. Copyright © 1943 by Howard Fast. Reprinted by permission of Grove/Atlantic, Inc.

Random House Children's Books: Excerpt from *Our Independence and the Constitution* by Dorothy Canfield Fisher. Copyright © 1950 by Dorothy Canfield Fisher. Copyright renewed 1978 by Sarah J. Scott. Reprinted by permission of Random House Children's Books, a division of Random House, Inc.

Printed in the United States of America

ISBN 0-618-19395-2

3 4 5 6 7 8 9 - DWI - 04 03

Contents

CHAPTER 8 Confederation to Constitution, 1776–1791

CONSTITUTION HANDBOOK

Chapter **6** *The Road to Revolution*

Setting the Stage

Reading Strategy: Sequencing Events

Imagine you are watching a baseball game on TV. The sports announcer gives a play-by-play account of the game's events as they unfold. These series of related actions are told in **sequence,** or the order in which they happened.

Think of this history chapter as a series of key plays that occur between opposing "teams"—the British and the American colonists. As you read, fill out the sequence chain below. Record the main events related to the growing conflict between these two sides. Use the dates mentioned in the chapter to help you keep the events in order.

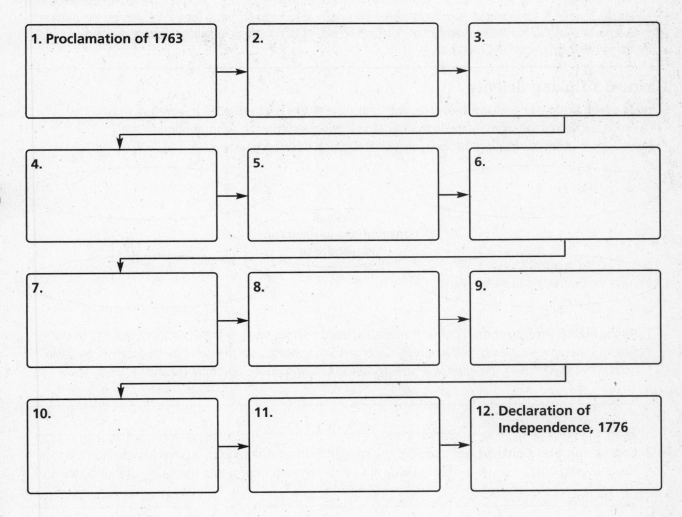

1. Proclamation of 1763

2.

3.

4.

5.

6.

7.

8.

9.

10.

11.

12. Declaration of Independence, 1776

Discussion Questions

1. Which boxes in your chart show British actions? Which show American colonists' actions?

2. Which boxes in your chart show a cause-and-effect relationship between two events?

3. If you could name the one event that changed the course of history, which would it be?

Name _____ Date _____

Tracing Themes

Theme: Impact of the Individual	Chapter Connection
American history is the story of individuals who through their actions have shaped events both at home and around the world.	From Samuel Adams to Thomas Jefferson, individuals with courage and vision led the colonists against British rule, and they ultimately declared their independence.

Tracing Themes Through U.S. History
From the earliest colonial settlements through today, heroic individuals have played an important role in shaping the nation. In Chapter 3, for example, John Smith saved the colony at Jamestown, while John Winthrop led the thriving Massachusetts Bay Colony. Other examples of outstanding individual achievement appear in many chapters, including Abraham Lincoln in Chapter 17.

Critical Thinking Activity

Create a web like the one shown below to highlight some of the key individuals involved in the American Revolution. Identify the individuals and explain each person's contribution to the colonial effort. After completing the web, answer the critical thinking questions.

Individual Contributions to American Independence

Thomas Jefferson— Writes the Declaration of Independence

1. **Recognizing Propaganda** Thomas Paine is believed to have swayed thousands of colonists to the side of independence with his pamphlet, *Common Sense*. Based on the pamphlet's excerpts on page 163, why do you think the work was so effective in shaping public opinion? Explain.

_____

_____

2. **Comparing and Contrasting** Consider the roles of Samuel Adams and Thomas Jefferson in the struggle with Britain. In what different way did each man help to promote the cause of independence?

_____

_____

3. **Forming and Supporting Opinions** Which individual on your graphic do you think played the most important role in the struggle against Britain? Support your answer with details from the chapter.

_____

_____

Name _____ Date _____

Guided Reading

A. Solving Problems As you read this section, fill in the second column of the chart below with more details about the British attempts to solve their problems. In the third column, explain how the colonists responded to each of those solutions.

Britain's Problems	Britain's Solutions		Colonists' Responses
1. Preventing Native American uprisings	Proclamation Act (1763):	→	
2. Keeping peace in the American colonies	Quartering Act (1765):	→	
3. Paying for war debts	Sugar Act (1764):	→	
	Stamp Act (1765):	→	
4. Maintaining power over the American colonies	Declaratory Act (1766):	→	

B. Summarizing On the back of this paper, briefly explain the importance of each of the following in protesting British policies.

Patrick Henry   boycott   Sons of Liberty

Chapter **6** *Section 2 Colonial Resistance Grows*

Guided Reading

A. Finding Main Ideas As you read pages 148–149 of this section, fill in the cluster diagrams with historical events, examples, or people that relate to the main idea questions below.

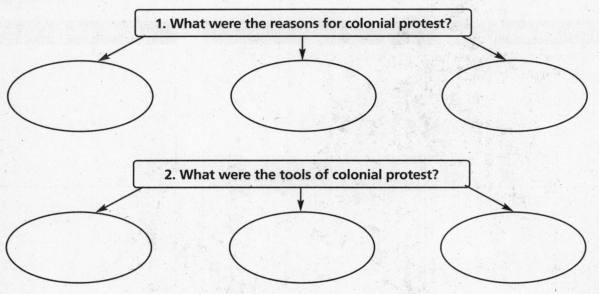

1. What were the reasons for colonial protest?

2. What were the tools of colonial protest?

B. Analyzing Causes and Recognizing Effects Fill out the cause-and-effect diagram to analyze the following British actions.

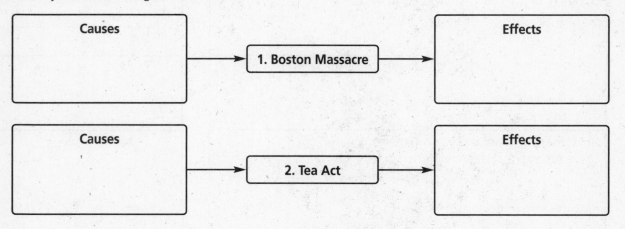

| Causes | 1. Boston Massacre | Effects |

| Causes | 2. Tea Act | Effects |

C. Forming and Supporting Opinions Fill in the chart to explain why you either approve or disapprove of the Boston Tea Party as a method of protest.

1. Your Opinion of the Boston Tea Party	2. Supporting Reasons a. b. c.

Guided Reading

A. Sequencing Events As you read this section, answer the questions about events shown in the time line below.

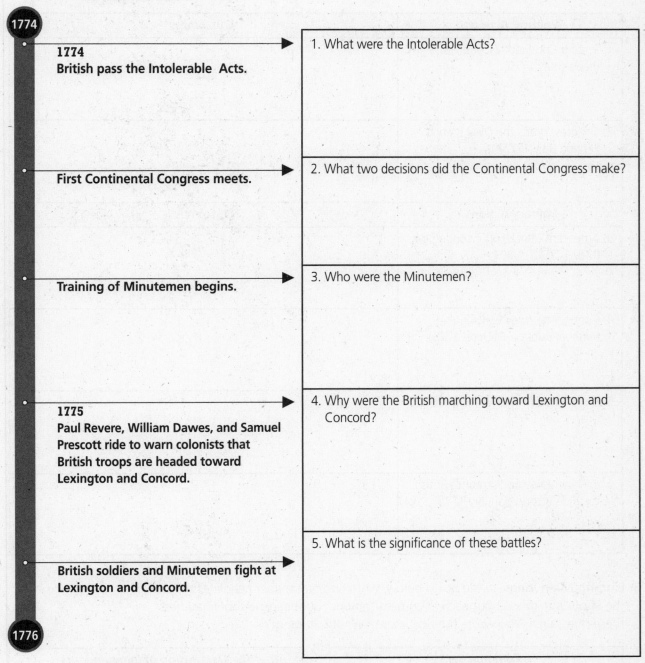

1774

1774
British pass the Intolerable Acts.

1. What were the Intolerable Acts?

First Continental Congress meets.

2. What two decisions did the Continental Congress make?

Training of Minutemen begins.

3. Who were the Minutemen?

1775
Paul Revere, William Dawes, and Samuel Prescott ride to warn colonists that British troops are headed toward Lexington and Concord.

4. Why were the British marching toward Lexington and Concord?

British soldiers and Minutemen fight at Lexington and Concord.

5. What is the significance of these battles?

1776

B. Analyzing Points of View On the back of this paper, briefly explain the sides that Patriots and Loyalists took during the Revolutionary War.

Name _____ Date _____

Guided Reading

A. Categorizing As you read this section, fill in the chart below with information about Americans' political and military actions at the outbreak of the Revolutionary War.

Political Actions	Outcomes
1. Second Continental Congress meets (May 1775).	
2. Congress drafts the Olive Branch Petition (July 1775).	

Military Actions	Outcomes
3. Americans attack Fort Ticonderoga (May 1775).	
4. Continental Army fights in the Battle of Bunker Hill (June 1775).	
5. Continental Army invades Quebec (November 1775).	
6. Continental Army surrounds British forces in Boston (January 1776).	

B. Finding Main Ideas In the boxes below, write two newspaper headlines that tell the important ideas about each document shown. Your headline should address these questions: Who wrote the document? What is it about?

Common Sense	The Declaration of Independence
1.	2.

Name _____ Date _____

Chapter 6 *The Declaration of Independence*

Guided Reading

A. Finding Main Ideas As you read the Declaration of Independence, fill in the
diagram below with key points about the main parts of the document.

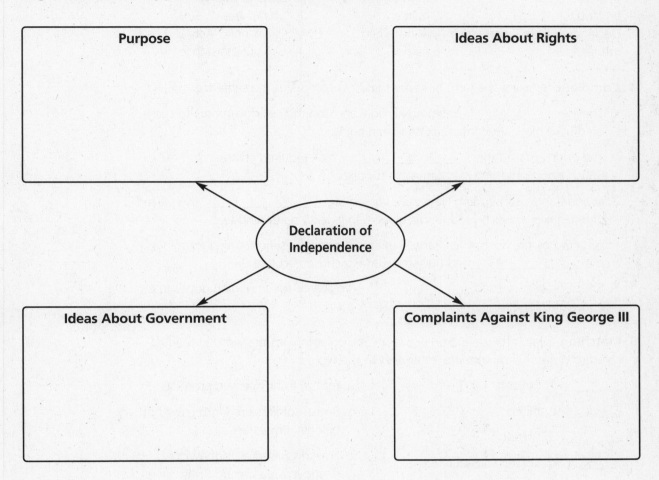

Purpose

Ideas About Rights

**Declaration of
Independence**

Ideas About Government

Complaints Against King George III

B. Evaluating Review the complaints against King George III that you listed in the box
above. Using a number scale, rate the complaints from most important to least
important. Record your numbers in the box.

C. Forming and Supporting Opinions Which part of the Declaration do you think is
the most meaningful for today? Explain why on the back of this paper.

Chapter 6 The Road to Revolution

Building Vocabulary

Boston Massacre	Lexington/Concord	Quartering Act
Boston Tea Party	Loyalist	Sons of Liberty
boycott	militia	Stamp Act
Declaration of Independence	Minutemen	Townshend Acts
Intolerable Acts	Patriot	writs of assistance

A. Completion Select the term or name that best completes the sentence.

1. The _____ required all legal and commercial documents to carry an official mark showing a tax had been paid.

2. The British passed the _____, which required colonists to house British troops and provide them with supplies.

3. In addition to suspending New York's assembly, _____ also placed import taxes on such products as glass, paper, lead, paint, and tea.

4. Angered by the Boston Tea Party, Parliament passed a series of laws known as the _____ to punish the Massachusetts colony.

5. British officers needed _____ to search for smuggled goods in a home or business.

B. Matching Match the definition in the second column with the word in the first column. Write the appropriate letter next to the word.

_____ 1. boycott

_____ 2. militia

_____ 3. Patriot

_____ 4. Boston Massacre

_____ 5. Lexington/Concord

_____ 6. Declaration of Independence

_____ 7. Sons of Liberty

_____ 8. Boston Tea Party

_____ 9. Loyalist

_____ 10. Minutemen

a. refusal to buy certain products

b. British soldiers fired into crowd of colonial protesters.

c. Men disguised as Mohawks destroyed tea aboard British ships.

d. force of armed civilians

e. militia trained to be ready quickly

f. supported the British

g. called for separation from Britain

h. secret society opposing the British

i. first battles of the Revolutionary War

j. supported the American colonists

C. Writing Use each of the following terms correctly in a letter to a friend or relative. Imagine that you live in Boston in 1776. Underline each word you use.

militia   boycott   Loyalist   Patriot   Minutemen

Name _____ Date _____

Skillbuilder Practice
Recognizing Propaganda

Before the Revolutionary War, both the British and the colonists used propaganda to influence public opinion. **Propaganda** is verbal or visual communication that is designed to influence a person's opinions, emotions, or actions. Visual propaganda uses symbols or images to influence a person's opinion. It often contains distortions of the truth.

Pictured to the right is **The American Rifle Men** from the British publication *Gentleman's and London Magazine,* published in March 1776. Examine the cartoon and think about which parts of it influence your opinion. Then answer the questions below. (See Skillbuilder Handbook, page R15.)

The American Rifle Men from *Gentleman's and London Magazine,* March, 1776.
Metropolitan Museum of Art. Bequest of Charles Allen Munn, 1924.

Propaganda Techniques in the Cartoon	Explanation
Appeal to prejudice	Judges groups of people according to a commonly held stereotype, such as all teenagers watch many hours of television
Attacking the person instead of the issue	Targets a person or a group of people, rather than an issue or problem
Distortion of the truth	Presents information that is only partially true

1. What British attitude toward Americans does this cartoon reveal? _____

_____

2. Does the cartoon target people or issues? Explain. _____

_____

3. How does the cartoon distort the truth about American soldiers? _____

_____

Geography Application
Historic Boston—1775 and Today

Boston was the early center of colonists' protest against British rule. It is no surprise, then, that several important landmarks of rebellion and armed conflict connected to the Revolutionary War are found in the area today. The site of the Boston Massacre attracts visitors to Boston. The Old North Church, from which the lantern signaled Paul Revere, still stands. A monument placed on Breed's Hill honors the colonists' moral victory at the Battle of Bunker Hill.

However, Boston has changed greatly since 1775. The city was once almost fragile—a small peninsula joined to the mainland by only a thin strip of land. Then landfill projects begun in the 1800s greatly expanded Boston. Also, nearby cities such as Charlestown were made part of greater Boston. As a result, citizens of 1775 would not recognize 21st-century Boston until they located historical sites and monuments in the older areas. The map below shows the more than 200-year change in Boston.

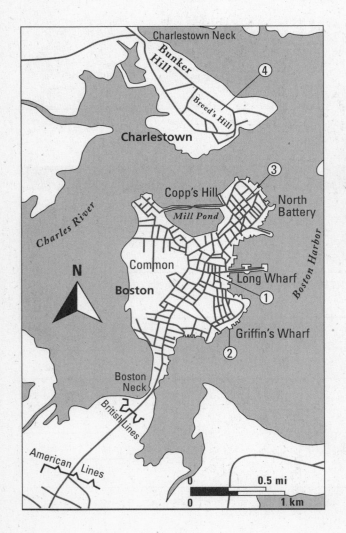

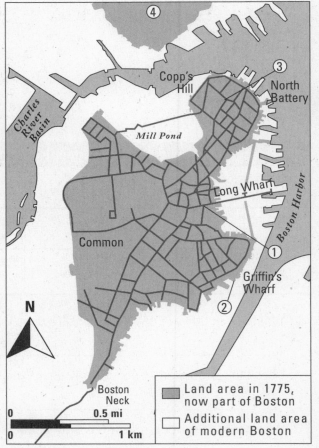

Land area in 1775, now part of Boston

Additional land area of modern Boston

Historical Sites for Both Maps
1. Boston Massacre
2. Boston Tea Party
3. Old North Church
4. Battle of Bunker Hill

Interpreting Maps and Text

1. In general, how has Boston changed from 1775 to today?

   _____

   _____

   _____

2. What area of old Boston has been the least altered by landfill?

   _____

   _____

3. Judging from the maps, which of the four historic sites seems the most altered today? Why?

   _____

   _____

   _____

4. About how far apart are the sites of the Boston Massacre and Boston Tea Party?

   _____

5. In 1775, what geographical features did Boston and neighboring Charlestown share?

   _____

   _____

6. Why do you think the British were particularly alarmed by colonial fortified positions on Breed's Hill?

   _____

   _____

   _____

7. Find the short "British Lines" on the southern end of the 1775 map. How would you judge their ability to protect Boston from land assault by the Americans?

   _____

   _____

   _____

Primary Source

Resolutions of the Stamp Act Congress

The strongest issue of debate among the 27 delegates at the Stamp Act Congress was whether to soften the rebellious tone of the resolutions. Below are some of the significant resolutions of the Stamp Act Congress.

The members of this Congress . . . esteem it our indispensable[1] duty to make the following declarations of our humble opinion, respecting the most essential rights and liberties of the colonists, and of the grievances under which they labour, by reason of several late Acts of Parliament.

I.   That His Majesty's subjects in these colonies, owe the same allegiance to the Crown of Great Britain, that is owing from his subjects born within the realm, and all due subordination[2] to that august[3] body the Parliament of Great Britain.

II. That His Majesty's liege[4] subjects in these colonies, are entitled to all the inherent[5] rights and liberties of his natural born subjects within the kingdom of Great Britain.

III. That it is inseparably essential to the freedom of a people, and the undoubted right of Englishmen, that no taxes be imposed[6] on them, but with their own consent, given personally, or by their representatives.

IV. That the people of these colonies are not, and from their local circumstances can not be, represented in the House of Commons in Great Britain.

V.   That the only representatives of the people of these colonies, are persons chosen therein by themselves, and that no taxes ever have been, or can be constitutionally imposed on them, but by their respective legislatures. . . .

VIII. That the late Act of Parliament, entitled, An Act for granting and applying certain Stamp Duties, and other Duties, in the British colonies and plantations in America, etc., by imposing taxes on the inhabitants of these colonies . . . [has] a manifest[7] tendency to subvert[8] the rights and liberties of the colonists. . . .

XI. That the restrictions imposed by several late Acts of Parliament, on the trade of these colonies, will render them unable to purchase the manufactures[9] of Great Britain. . . .

Lastly, That it is the indispensable duty of these colonies . . . to endeavour[10] by a loyal and dutiful address to his Majesty, and humble applications to both Houses of Parliament, to procure the repeal of the Act for granting and applying certain stamp duties.

from "Resolutions of the Stamp Act Congress," in *Great Issues in American History,* Vol. I, ed. by Richard Hofstadter (New York: Vintage, 1958).

---

1. indispensable: essential.
2. subordination: to put in a lower class or rank.
3. august: inspiring awe or admiration.
4. liege: loyal, faithful.
5. inherent: existing as an essential part.
6. imposed: to establish or apply as compulsory.
7. manifest: obvious.
8. subvert: to destroy completely.
9. manufactures: products.
10. endeavour: serious attempt or effort.

Main Ideas

1. What right of all Englishmen did the colonists claim for themselves?

2. Why did the Congress believe that the English Parliament had no right to impose a tax on them?

Critical Thinking

3. **Making Inferences** Which resolution contained the threat of a boycott? Explain.

4. **Drawing Conclusions** Which resolution was designed to ease the fears of the king and Parliament?

Chapter **6** Section 4 Declaring Independence

Primary Source
Letter from Abigail Adams

Beginning in the 1760s, Abigail Adams (1744–1818) wrote hundreds of letters to her husband John Adams, her four children, her relatives, and her friends. These letters gave a vivid picture of life in 18th-century America. Adams described her duties as a wife, parent, and friend. She also voiced her opinions on politics and society. She wrote the following letter to John Adams the day after the Battle of Bunker Hill. It shows her concern over the outcome of the battle.

Abigail Adams to John Adams, Sunday June 18, 1775

Dearest Friend,

  The Day; perhaps the decisive Day is come on which the fate of America depends. My bursting Heart must find vent[1] at my pen. I have just heard that our dear Friend Dr. Warren is no more but fell gloriously fighting for his Country—saying better to die honourably in the field than ignominiously[2] hang upon the Gallows.[3] Great is our Loss. He has distinguished himself in every engagement, by his courage and fortitude,[4] by animating the Soldiers and leading them on by his own example. A particular account of these dreadful, but I hope Glorious Days will be transmitted you, no doubt in the exactest manner.

  The race is not to the swift, nor the battle to the strong, but the God of Israel is he that giveth strength and power unto his people. Trust in him at all times, ye people pour out your hearts before him. God is a refuge for us.—Charlestown[5] is laid in ashes. The Battle began upon our intrenchments[6] upon Bunkers Hill, a Saturday morning about 3 o'clock and has not ceased yet and tis now 3 o'clock Sabbeth afternoon.

  Tis expected they will come out over the Neck tonight, and a dreadful Battle must ensue. Almighty God cover the heads of our Country men, and be a shield to our Dear Friends. How [many ha]ve fallen we know not—the constant roar of the cannon is so [distre]ssing that we can not Eat, Drink or Sleep. May we be supported and sustaind in the dreadful conflict. I shall tarry[7] here til tis thought unsafe by my Friends,

and then I have secured myself a retreat at your Brothers who has kindly offerd me part of his house. I cannot compose myself to write any further at present. I will add more as I hear further.

  —I am most sincerely yours,
  Abigail Adams

1. **vent:** means of escape or release.
2. **ignominiously:** marked by shame or disgrace.
3. **Gallows:** two upright posts supporting a crossbeam from which a noose hangs; is used for execution.
4. **fortitude:** strength to endure pain.
5. **Charlestown:** town next to Boston, where the Battle of Bunker Hill was fought.
6. **intrenchments:** defensive positions.
7. **tarry:** to delay or be late.

Main Ideas

1. Why does Adams choose to write this letter?

2. According to Adams, how long has the Battle of Bunker Hill lasted so far?

Critical Thinking

3. **Drawing Conclusions** Who does Adams say people should trust to determine the outcome of the battle? What does this indicate about her?

4. **Analyzing Points of View** Why do you think Adams is considering moving to another house?

Name _____   Date _____

Literature Selection

Paul Revere's Ride by Henry Wadsworth Longfellow

The most popular American poet of his time, Henry Wadsworth Longfellow (1807–1882) told the story of Paul Revere's famous ride in this poem. Revere's ride took place on April 18, 1775. His job was to spread news about British troop movements. Longfellow's poem was first published in 1863, nearly 90 years after the event. The poem's historical accuracy has been questioned, but Longfellow nevertheless turned Paul Revere into a legend.

Listen, my children, and you shall hear
Of the midnight ride of Paul Revere,
On the eighteenth of April, in Seventy-five;
Hardly a man is now alive
5   Who remembers that famous day and year.

He said to his friend, "If the British march
By land or sea from the town to-night,
Hang a lantern aloft in the belfry arch[1]
Of the North Church tower as a signal light,—
10   One if by land, and two if by sea;
And I on the opposite shore will be,
Ready to ride and spread the alarm
Through every Middlesex[2] village and farm,
For the country folk to be up and to arm."

15   Then he said, "Good-night!" and with muffled oar
Silently rowed to the Charlestown shore,
Just as the moon rose over the bay,
Where swinging wide at her moorings[3] lay
The *Somerset,* British man-of-war;[4]
20   A phantom ship, with each mast and spar[5]
Across the moon like a prison bar,
And a huge black hulk, that was magnified
By its own reflection in the tide.

Meanwhile, his friend, through alley and street
25   Wanders and watches, with eager ears,
Till in the silence around him he hears
The muster of men at the barrack door,
The sound of arms, and the tramp of feet,

---

1. **belfry** (BEHL•free) **arch**: a curved opening in a bell tower.
2. **Middlesex:** a county of eastern Massachusetts, setting for the first battle of the Revolutionary War on April 19, 1775.
3. **moorings:** the place where a ship is docked.
4. **man-of-war:** warship.
5. **spar:** a pole supporting a ship's sail.

And the measured tread of the grenadiers,[6]
30 Marching down to their boats on the shore.

Then he climbed the tower of the Old North Church,
By the wooden stairs, with stealthy tread,[7]
To the belfry chamber overhead,
And startled the pigeons from their perch
35 On the somber[8] rafters, that round him made
Masses and moving shapes of shade,—
By the trembling ladder, steep and tall,
To the highest window in the wall,
Where he paused to listen and look down
40 A moment on the roofs of the town
And the moonlight flowing over all.

Beneath, in the churchyard, lay the dead,
In their night encampment on the hill,
Wrapped in silence so deep and still
45 That he could hear, like a sentinel's[9] tread,
The watchful night-wind, as it went
Creeping along from tent to tent,
And seeming to whisper, "All is well!"
A moment only he feels the spell
50 Of the place and the hour, and the secret dread
Of the lonely belfry and the dead;
For suddenly all his thoughts are bent
On a shadowy something far away,
Where the river widens to meet the bay,—
55 A line of black that bends and floats
On the rising tide like a bridge of boats.

Meanwhile, impatient to mount and ride,
Booted and spurred, with a heavy stride
On the opposite shore walked Paul Revere.
60 Now he patted his horse's side,
Now he gazed at the landscape far and near,
Then, impetuous,[10] stamped the earth,
And turned and tightened his saddle girth;[11]
But mostly he watched with eager search

---

6. grenadiers (grehn•uh•DEERZ): foot soldiers.
7. stealthy tread: quiet footsteps.
8. somber: gloomy.
9. sentinel: a guard or sentry.
10. impetuous (ihm•PEHCH•oo•uhs): acting suddenly, on impulse.
11. saddle girth: the strap attaching a saddle to a horse's body.

65   The belfry tower of the Old North Church,
      As it rose above the graves on the hill,
      Lonely and spectral[12] and somber and still.
      And lo! as he looks, on the belfry's height
      A glimmer, and then a gleam of light!
70   He springs to the saddle, the bridle he turns,
      But lingers and gazes, till full on his sight
      A second lamp in the belfry burns.

      A hurry of hoofs in a village street,
      A shape in the moonlight, a bulk in the dark,
75   And beneath, from the pebbles, in passing, a spark
      Struck out by a steed flying fearless and fleet;
      That was all! And yet, through the gloom and the light,
      The fate of a nation was riding that night;
      And the spark struck out by that steed, in his flight,
80   Kindled the land into flame with its heat.
      He has left the village and mounted the steep,
      And beneath him, tranquil and broad and deep,
      Is the Mystic,[13] meeting the ocean tides;
      And under the alders[14] that skirt its edge,
85   Now soft on the sand, now loud on the ledge,
      Is heard the tramp of his steed as he rides.

      It was twelve by the village clock,
      When he crossed the bridge into Medford town.
      He heard the crowing of the cock,
90   And the barking of the farmer's dog,
      And felt the damp of the river fog,
      That rises after the sun goes down.

      It was one by the village clock,
      When he galloped into Lexington.
95   He saw the gilded weathercock
      Swim in the moonlight as he passed,
      And the meeting-house windows, blank and bare,
      Gaze at him with a spectral glare,
      As if they already stood aghast[15]
100   At the bloody work they would look upon.

---

12. **spectral:** ghostly.
13. **Mystic:** a short river flowing into Boston Harbor.
14. **alders:** trees of the birch family.
15. **aghast** (uh•GAST): terrified.

It was two by the village clock,
When he came to the bridge in Concord town.
He heard the bleating[16] of the flock,
And the twitter of birds among the trees,
105 And felt the breath of the morning breeze
Blowing over the meadow brown.
And one was safe and asleep in his bed
Who at the bridge would be first to fall,
Who that day would be lying dead,
110 Pierced by a British musket-ball.

You know the rest. In the books you have read
How the British Regulars[17] fired and fled,—
How the farmers gave them ball for ball,
From behind each fence and farmyard wall,
115 Chasing the redcoats down the lane,
Then crossing the fields to emerge again
Under the trees at the turn of the road,
And only pausing to fire and load.

So through the night rode Paul Revere;
120 And so through the night went his cry of alarm
To every Middlesex village and farm,—
A cry of defiance, and not of fear,
A voice in the darkness, a knock at the door,
And a word that shall echo forevermore!
125 For, borne on the night-wind of the Past,
Through all our history, to the last,
In the hour of darkness and peril[18] and need,
The people will waken and listen to hear
The hurrying hoof-beats of that steed,
130 And the midnight message of Paul Revere.

---

16. **bleating:** the crying of sheep.
17. **British Regulars:** members of Great Britain's standing army.
18. **peril:** danger.

Main Ideas

1. What is the setting of this poem, and who are its main characters?

2. What was Revere's plan for announcing the movement of the British troops?

Critical Thinking

3. **Comparing and Contrasting** How does the account in this poem differ from the account of Revere's ride in the text? Explain.

4. **Drawing Conclusions** What do the last lines of the poem reveal about Longfellow's purpose for writing it?

Reteaching Activity

Analyzing Points of View

Write **C** in the blank if the phrase describes the colonists, or **B** if the phrase describes the British in the years after the French and Indian War.

_____ 1. Enacted the Proclamation of 1763 to stop settlement west of the Appalachian Mountains

_____ 2. Forced to house soldiers under the Quartering Act

_____ 3. Forced to buy stamps for legal papers and other items

_____ 4. Opposed taxation without representation

_____ 5. Organized the Stamp Act Congress

_____ 6. Organized a boycott to protest tax policies

_____ 7. Organized secret societies such as the Sons of Liberty

_____ 8. Repealed the Stamp Act in response to merchants' complaints

_____ 9. Passed the Declaratory Act regarding the making of laws for the colonies

_____ 10. Burned stamped paper and covered customs officials with hot tar and feathers

Name _____ Date _____

Reteaching Activity

Finding Main Ideas

Some of the headings from the section are shown below. Rewrite each of the headings as a question. Then answer the question in your own words. Part of the first question has been shown as an example.

1. **Heading:** Townshend Acts Are Passed

   Question: How did the Townshend Acts affect the colonies?

   Answer: _____

2. **Heading:** Reasons for Protests

   Question: _____

   Answer: _____

3. **Heading:** Tools of Protest

   Question: _____

   Answer: _____

4. **Heading:** The Boston Massacre

   Question: _____

   Answer: _____

5. **Heading:** The Tea Act

   Question: _____

   Answer: _____

6. **Heading:** The Boston Tea Party

   Question: _____

   Answer: _____

Name _____ Date _____

Reteaching Activity

Finding Main Ideas

The following questions deal with events that led up to the American Revolution. Answer them in the space provided.

1. What was King George's reaction to the Boston Tea Party?

_____

_____

2. When were the Intolerable Acts passed? List their four parts.

_____

_____

3. When did the First Continental Congress meet? What actions did it take?

_____

_____

4. Why did colonists expect Parliament to repeal the Intolerable Acts? What did Parliament do instead?

_____

_____

5. When did Patrick Henry deliver a stirring speech to the Virginia Convention? What was his message?

_____

_____

6. When did British troops march on Lexington and Concord? How were colonists alerted to the British moves? How did the colonists resist the British? _____

_____

_____

Reteaching Activity

Making Inferences

Read each clue below and answer the question "Who am I?" Write your answer in the blank.

1. I wrote many letters to my husband and was a sharp observer of the political scene.

   WHO AM I? _____

2. I captured Fort Ticonderoga with a band of men known as the Green Mountain Boys.

   WHO AM I? _____

3. I was chosen as the commanding general of the Continental Army.

   WHO AM I? _____

4. I led 2,200 soldiers in an attack on Breed's Hill.

   WHO AM I? _____

5. I defended Breed's Hill and told my men, "Don't fire until you see the whites of their eyes!"

   WHO AM I? _____

6. I was America's first important African-American poet. I was born in Africa and sold into slavery as a child.

   WHO AM I? _____

7. I wanted to defeat British forces in Quebec in eastern Canada to gain Canadian support for the revolution.

   WHO AM I? _____

8. I wrote *Common Sense,* a pamphlet that convinced many Americans that a complete break with Britain was necessary.

   WHO AM I? _____

9. I wrote the Declaration of Independence, which was based on the philosophy of John Locke.

   WHO AM I? _____

10. I was the first to sign the Declaration and urged the delegates to stand together in mutual defense.

   WHO AM I? _____

Enrichment Activity

Debating Independence

Activity Imagine you are a delegate to the Continental Congress. Form two teams and stage a debate for the class in which you argue for or against declaring independence from Britain. **Winning Strategies for Debate**. A debate is a structured argument. The basis of a debate is the proposition, a formal statement of the issue to be debated. One team of debaters argues for the proposition. The negative team argues against it. Both sides create a brief, or a complete outline of the debate. They also prepare a rebuttal, or a follow-up speech, that supports their own arguments and attacks those of their opponents. Follow these guidelines to plan and conduct your debate.

---

1. Preparing for the Debate

- **Gather information.** Research the Patriots' and Loyalists' views on the issue of declaring independence. Record key ideas for both sides on note cards, with one note per card.

- **Rank key ideas.** Build your case by arranging the points of the opposing team's arguments and your own in order of importance.

- **Support your argument.** Find facts, expert opinions, quotations, and examples that defend your position and challenge that of your opponents.

- **Write the brief.** To write a brief, restate the proposition. Then list the arguments and evidence that support both sides.

2. Conducting the Debate

- **Present your case.** For each team, allow five minutes for members to deliver summaries of their arguments.

- **Play fair.** Show respect by listening to all speakers and not interrupting.

3. Presenting a Rebuttal

- **Target weaknesses in the opposing team's arguments.** The rebuttal is your chance to undermine your opponents' position. Listen carefully and look for missing evidence or unclear arguments.

- **Offer counter arguments.** Refer to the information that you have gathered about your opponents' weaknesses. Present additional evidence that supports your side.

4. Determining the winning position.

- Ask each classroom audience member to vote for a position based on how convincing the arguments were.

Reflect and Assess

At the end of the debate, discuss the debate process you followed—and the conclusions reached—with the class. Explore the ideas and issues below.

- Was the process used orderly and predictable?

- Were arguments logical and well-supported?

- What changes in the process might improve it?

Name _____ Date _____

History Workshop Resources
Raise the Liberty Pole

Follow the instructions in your textbook on pages 172–173 to construct a liberty pole and 13 colonial flags. As you read the chart below about the 13 colonies, look for words that form pictures in your mind. These images can help you think of designs to draw on your colonial flags.

New England Colonies	Economic Activities	Interesting Facts
Massachusetts (including Maine)	shipbuilding, shipping, fishing, whaling, lumber, silversmithing, trading	During the Boston Tea Party of 1773, Patriots protested the Tea Act by dumping 342 chests of tea into Boston Harbor.
New Hampshire	ship masts, lumber, fishing, trading	New Hampshire was the first colony to draft its own constitution—about six months before the signing of the Declaration of Independence.
Connecticut	shipping, livestock	Connecticut's state song is "Yankee Doodle Dandy."
Rhode Island	ironmaking, whaling, shipbuilding, livestock, dairy industry	Some religious groups built their first houses of worship in America here—the first Baptist church (1729), first Seventh Day Adventist church (1729), and the first synagogue (1763).
Middle Colonies		
New York	furs, wheat, flour mills, glassmaking, livestock, shipping, shipbuilding	Peter Zenger's trial, held in New York City in 1735, advanced the cause of liberty—the freedom of newspapers to print the truth and criticize government policies.
Delaware	trade, wheat, corn, rye, dairy products	Swedish colonists built the first log cabins here.
New Jersey	trade, cattle, wheat, corn, rye, dairy products, copper	Many Quakers settled in New Jersey. Among them was John Woolman (1720–1772), who took a stand against slavery and expressed his respect for Native Americans.
Pennsylvania	furs, paper, iron, wheat, flour mills, flax, shipbuilding	The Liberty Bell first rang in Philadelphia on July 8, 1776, to celebrate the Declaration of Independence.
Southern Colonies		
North Carolina	oak timber for shipbuilding, tobacco, furs	Pirates struck terror along the coast of North Carolina. In 1718, the pirate Blackbeard was captured there.
Virginia	tobacco, wheat, cattle, iron	Virginia was the birthplace of great colonial leaders—George Washington, Thomas Jefferson, Patrick Henry, and James Madison.
Maryland	tobacco, wheat	The Toleration Act, passed by the Maryland legislature in 1649, was an important step toward religious freedom in the colonies. Maryland became a haven for Roman Catholics and other religious groups.
South Carolina	rice, indigo, silk	In 1744, Eliza Lucas Pinckney cultivated the first thriving indigo plant in the colonies. Three years later, indigo became one of South Carolina's major exports.
Georgia	rice, indigo, oak timber for shipbuilding, lumber	The luxurious mansions on Georgia's rice plantations often had wide porches, huge halls, and elegant staircases.

Geography Connections Review the following maps from your textbook to help you think of more ideas for colonial flags.

- "The New England Colonies," page 94
- "The Middle Colonies," page 99
- "The Southern Colonies," page 104
- "Geography in History—Differences Among the Colonies," pages 108–109

Chapter **7** *The American Revolution*

Setting the Stage

Reading Strategy: Sequencing Events

Like a road map guiding a driver on a car trip, a time line can help you chart your course as you journey back in history. A time line gives you a sense of direction by organizing the **sequence,** or time order, of events.

   Imagine your destination is the American Revolution. As you read the chapter, track the major battles and events of the war on the time line below. Review your completed time line to picture the action that occurred from 1776 to 1783.

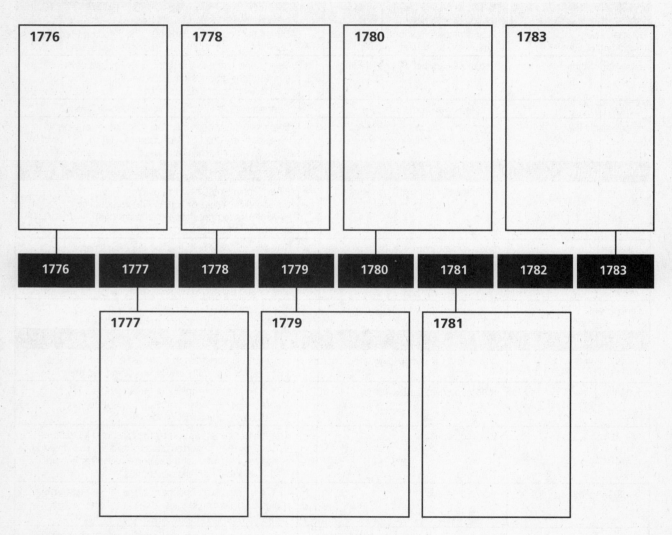

Discussion Questions

1. What hardships were endured by American soldiers beginning in late 1777? How do you picture this situation?

2. When did France become America's ally? What was one outcome of this alliance?

3. In what year did British forces move south? What three important battles did the British win there?

Chapter **7** *The American Revolution*

Tracing Themes

Theme: Citizenship	Chapter Connection
The study of American history—as seen through the actions of American citizens—provides models of the rights and responsibilities of citizenship.	During the Revolutionary War, many Americans saw themselves as citizens of a new country and took enormous risks for the cause of independence.

Tracing Themes Through U.S. History
Throughout American history, many people have fought for the rights of American citizens. For example, in Chapter 14 abolitionists fought to end slavery. In the Chapter 19 Epilogue, progressives tried to make government more democratic.

Critical Thinking Activity

Create a chart like the one below to show examples of citizenship during the Revolutionary War. For each individual or group listed in the chart, describe actions that reflect the values of citizenship. After completing the chart, answer the critical thinking questions.

Citizenship During the Revolution	
Group/Individual	**Actions**
George Washington	led the army against great odds
Haym Salomon	
Patriot women	
Thomas Paine	
Valley Forge troops	
James Forten	

1. **Forming and Supporting Opinions** Benedict Arnold—a great hero in the early years of the Revolution—betrayed the Patriot cause when he felt his actions weren't rewarded. Should a person expect rewards for being a good citizen? Support your opinion.

_____

2. **Analyzing Points of View** During the Revolution, both Patriots and Loyalists considered that their positions and views were honorable. How might people on both sides have felt that they were being good citizens?

_____

3. **Identifying Facts and Opinions** Identify one fact and one opinion in the following statement: Citizens in a republic should be required to vote because republican government gets its authority from the people. Explain your answer.

_____

In-Depth Resources: Unit 2

Chapter 7 Section 1 The Early Years of the War

Guided Reading

A. Categorizing Use the chart below to take notes about who chose the Patriot side and who chose the Loyalist side.

Patriots	Loyalists

B. Analyzing Causes and Recognizing Effects As you read this section, write answers to the questions about each of the Revolutionary War battles listed below.

	Who won?	Why did they win?	What were the important results?
1. New York			
2. Trenton			
3. Saratoga			

Name _____ Date _____

Guided Reading

A. Categorizing As you read this section, take notes about people who helped to win American independence.

1. Marquis de Lafayette	2. Baron von Steuben
3. George Rogers Clark	4. John Paul Jones

B. Finding Main Ideas On the back of this paper, explain or define each of the following terms:

ally   privateer

Name _____   Date _____

Guided Reading

A. Analyzing Causes and Recognizing Effects As you read this section, write
answers to the questions about each of the Revolutionary War battles listed below.

	Who won?	Why did they win?	What were the important results?
1. Charles Town			
2. Camden			
3. Yorktown			

B. Summarizing What were the difficulties faced by each group of Patriots during the
Revolutionary War?

Patriots	What were some of the hardships they faced?
Civilians	
Soldiers	
Guerrilla Fighters	

C. Finding Main Ideas On the back of this paper, identify or define each of the
following terms.
Lord Cornwallis   pacifist

Name _____ Date _____

Chapter **7** Section 4 The Legacy of the War

Guided Reading

A. Analyzing Causes As you read this section, use the chart below to take notes about the advantages that led to America's victory.

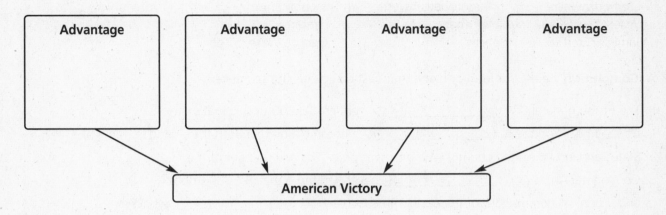

| Advantage | Advantage | Advantage | Advantage |

American Victory

B. Recognizing Effects Use the chart below to take notes about the legacy of the war.

Terms of the Treaty	Costs of the War	Issues After the War

Chapter **7** *The American Revolution*

Building Vocabulary

ally	guerrilla	privateer
bayonet	John Paul Jones	rendezvous
Lord Cornwallis	Marquis de Lafayette	republicanism
desert	mercenary	strategy
James Forten	pacifist	George Washington

A. Completion Select the term or name that best completes the sentence.

The British general (1) _____ surrendered 8,000 troops that were

trapped near Yorktown. (2) _____ became a hero in both the United

States and in France, the country where he was born. The commander of the

Continental Army, (3) _____, never had more than 17,000 troops

under him. As commander of the *Bonhomme Richard,* (4) _____ won

the most famous sea battle of the Revolutionary War. Among the many African

Americans who fought for independence was (5) _____.

B. Matching Match the definition in the second column with the word in the first column.
Write the appropriate letter next to the word.

_____ 1. ally   a. a ship permitted to attack enemy ships

_____ 2. mercenary   b. a person opposed to war

_____ 3. bayonet   c. an overall plan of action

_____ 4. privateer   d. the idea that the people should rule

_____ 5. rendezvous   e. a fighter who uses hit-and-run attacks

_____ 6. desert   f. a country that aids another country

_____ 7. pacifist   g. a soldier fighting for another country

_____ 8. republicanism h. a knife attached to a gun

_____ 9. strategy   i. to leave military duty without planning to return

_____ 10. guerrilla   j. a meeting

C. Writing Use each of the following terms correctly in analyzing France's role in the Revolutionary War.
Imagine you are an aide to General George Washington, and you are writing a report for him. Underline
each word you use.

ally	Battles of Saratoga	Treaty of Paris of 1783
Marquis de Lafayette	Battle of Yorktown	

Chapter **7** Section 1 *The Early Years of the War*

Skillbuilder Practice
Creating a Multimedia Presentation

A **multimedia presentation** draws from among several different kinds of media—including videos, CD-ROMs, and computer software—to create a single presentation. Follow the steps on this flowchart to develop a multimedia presentation about a topic from the early years of the American Revolution. (See Skillbuilder Handbook, page R33.)

1. Identify your audience. Consider their interests and their level of knowledge. What kinds of media might capture their attention? Consider the use of CD-ROMs or videos. Describe your audience:

_____

_____

2. Select a topic. Choose a topic you are curious about and that you can find information about easily. Be sure you can use different kinds of media to present your topic. Write your topic:

_____

_____

3. Brainstorm information you want to use. Think of what people might see, hear, and feel. In some cases, you might consider what they will taste and smell. Consider the use of slides, posters, or audio tapes as well as the media previously mentioned. Describe the main types of information you will use:

_____

_____

_____

4. Gather and organize your information. Consider which elements of your presentation you want viewers to focus on. Don't overwhelm your audience with too much technology. Choose a few types of media and keep the presentation simple.

5. Display your presentation. Listen to comments from your classmates as they view it.

Chapter **7** Section 3 The Path to Victory

Geography Application

Cornwallis Is Trapped at Yorktown, 1781

By 1781, General Cornwallis's troops were wearing down under pressure from Greene's and Lafayette's armies. So Cornwallis retreated into Virginia to regroup.

But Cornwallis made a poor decision. He set up his base at Yorktown, on the inner shores of Chesapeake Bay. He had expected that his troops could be reinforced from New York by ships. However, he underestimated the French help to the American cause.

A large French fleet arrived from the West Indies. It sealed off the bay. Cornwallis could not get out by boat, and help from New York could not arrive quickly. Knowing this, French General Rochambeau joined Washington. Their combined armies rushed to cut off Cornwallis's southern and western routes.

Soon, American and French troops were dug in within 300 yards of the British. American cannon fire increased. Then Cornwallis made a bold nighttime attempt to cross the York River to a small encampment there. He had hoped to break out into the countryside and make his way to New York. A violent rainstorm, though, blew most of his boats back to the Yorktown shore. Three days later, on October 19, the British formally surrendered. It was the end of a relatively bloodless battle. The map below shows how impossible Cornwallis's situation was.

Back in England, the Yorktown defeat had great impact. Members of Parliament now had their best argument for finally granting America independence. The war was virtually over.

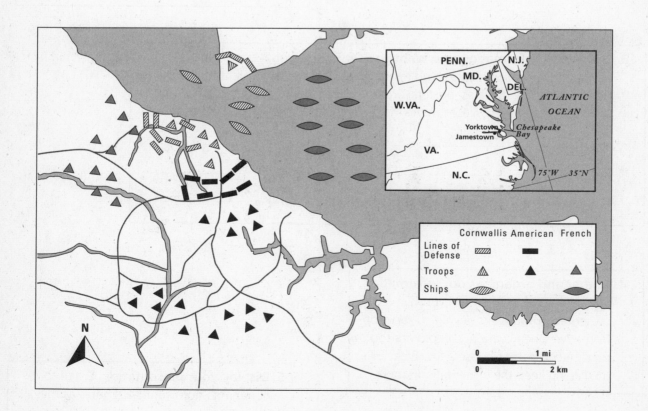

Interpreting Maps and Text

1. Where is Yorktown located?

   _____

   _____

2. What prevented British ships from sailing down the Atlantic coast to help Cornwallis?

   _____

   _____

3. What prevented Cornwallis's escape by land?

   _____

   _____

4. Who cut off Yorktown from the south?

   _____

   from the west?

   _____

5. Which of the three forces at Yorktown had no ships in the York River/Chesapeake Bay area?

   _____

6. Who controlled the small encampment on the shore opposite Yorktown?

   _____

7. About how far was the encampment from Yorktown?

   _____

8. What prevented Cornwallis's attempt to reach that shore under the cover of darkness?

   _____

9. Find Jamestown on the inset map. What is ironic, or surprisingly unusual, about Yorktown being so relatively close to it?

   _____

   _____

Primary Source
from *Private Yankee Doodle* by Joseph Plumb Martin

In 1776, at the age of 15, Joseph Plumb Martin joined a Connecticut regiment to fight for American independence in the Revolutionary War. During the war, he fought in many important battles, including Brooklyn, Monmouth, and Yorktown. In the first excerpt below, he describes his experiences at Valley Forge, Pennsylvania, in the winter of 1777–1778. In the second excerpt, Martin describes his experiences at the Battle of Monmouth in New Jersey, June 1778.

Valley Forge

Almost every one has heard of the soldiers of the Revolution being tracked by the blood of their feet on the frozen ground. This is literally true, and the thousandth part of their sufferings has not, nor ever will be told. . . . For on our march from the Valley Forge, through the Jerseys . . . a fourth part of the troops had not a scrip[1] of anything but their ragged shirt flaps to cover their nakedness. . . .

How often have I had to lie whole stormy, cold nights in a wood, on a field, or a bleak hill, with such blankets and other clothing like them, with nothing but the canopy[2] of the heavens to cover me. All this too in the heart of winter, when a New England farmer, if his cattle had been in my situation, would not have slept a wink from sheer anxiety[3] for them.

Battle of Monmouth

By this time the British had come in contact with the New England forces at the fence, when a sharp conflict ensued. . . .

We were immediately ordered from our old detachment and joined another, the whole composing a corps of about five hundred men. We instantly marched towards the enemy's right wing, which was in the orchard, and . . . into the open fields and formed our line. . . . As I passed through the orchard I saw a number of the enemy lying under the trees, killed by our fieldpiece.[4] . . .

The first shot they gave us from [a small piece of artillery] . . . cut off the thigh bone of a captain, just above the knee, and the whole heel of a private in the rear of him. . . . We then laid ourselves down under the fences and bushes to take a breath, for we had need of it. I presume everyone has heard of the heat of that day, but none can realize it that did not feel it. Fighting is

hot work in cool weather, how much more so in such weather as it was on the [28th] of June, 1778.

After the action in our part of the army had ceased, . . . I found [a] wounded captain . . . lying on the ground and begging his sergeant . . . to help him off the field or he should bleed to death. . . . I then offered to assist . . . in carrying him to a meetinghouse a short distance off, where the rest of the wounded men and surgeons were. . . . I . . . tarried[5] a few minutes to see the wounded and two or three limbs amputated.

from Joseph Plumb Martin, *Private Yankee Doodle,* ed. by George F. Scheer (Boston: Little, Brown, 1962). Reprinted in *The Revolutionaries* (Alexandria, Virginia: Time-Life Books, 1996).

1. **scrip:** scrap.
2. **canopy:** covering.
3. **anxiety:** worry.
4. **fieldpiece:** artillery.
5. **tarried:** waited.

Main Ideas

1. What problems did Martin and the other soldiers face at Valley Forge?

2. What did Martin find lying beneath the trees in the orchard?

Critical Thinking

3. **Forming Opinions** Why do you think Martin stayed with the army despite the problems he faced at Valley Forge?

4. **Sequencing Events** What was the order of events that Martin describes at the Battle of Monmouth?

Primary Source

An African-American Petition for Freedom

During the American Revolution, colonists fought for freedom from Great Britain. At the same time that colonists were demanding their freedom, they held 700,000 Africans and African Americans in slavery. Several of these enslaved people signed a petition requesting that Massachusetts grant them the liberty that the colonists wanted from Great Britain. The petition was submitted to the Massachusetts House of Representatives on January 13, 1777.

The petition of a great number of blacks detained in a state of slavery in the bowels[1] of a free and Christian country humbly shows that your petitioners apprehend[2] that they have in common with all other men a natural and unalienable right to that freedom which the Great Parent of the universe has bestowed equally on all mankind and which they have never forfeited by any compact or agreement whatever. But they were unjustly dragged by the hand of cruel power from their dearest friends and some of them even torn from the embraces of their tender parents, from a populous, pleasant, and plentiful country and in violation of laws of nature and of nations and in defiance of all the tender feelings of humanity, brought here either to be sold like beasts of burden and, like them, condemned to slavery for life— among a people professing the mild religion of Jesus; a people not insensible[3] of the secrets of rational being, nor without spirit to resent the unjust endeavors of others to reduce them to a state of bondage and subjection. Your Honor need not be informed that a life of slavery like that of your petitioners, deprived of every social privilege of everything requisite to render life tolerable, is far worse [than] nonexistence.

In imitation of the laudable example of the good people of these states, your petitioners have long and patiently awaited the event of petition after petition presented by them to the legislative body of this state, and cannot but with grief reflect that their success has been but too similar. They cannot but express their astonishment that it has never been considered that every principle from which America has acted in the course of their unhappy difficulties with Great Britain pleads stronger than a thousand arguments in favor of your petitioners.

They therefore humbly beseech Your Honors to give this petition its due weight and consideration, and cause an act of legislation to be passed whereby they may be restored to the enjoyments of that which is the natural right of all men, and that their children, who were born in this land of liberty, may not be held as slaves after they arrive at the age of [21] years. So may the inhabitants of this state, no longer chargeable with the inconsistency of acting themselves the part which they condemn and oppose in others, be prospered in their present glorious struggle for liberty and have those blessings for themselves.

from *Collections, Masachusetts Historical Society* (Cambridge and Boston, 1795). Reprinted in *Annals of America,* Vol. 2 (Chicago: Encyclopaedia Britannica,1968), 482–483.

1. **bowels:** the insides of.
2. **apprehend:** understand.
3. **insensible:** unaware.

Main Ideas

1. How were the signers of this petition "in imitation of the laudable example of the good people of these states?"

2. What plan for gradually ending slavery do the petitioners suggest?

Critical Thinking

3. **Drawing Conclusions** What do the petitioners mean when they say the people of their state have been "acting themselves the part which they condemn and oppose in others?"

4. **Comparing** How are the ideas expressed in the first sentence similar to those in the Declaration of Independence?

Literature Selection

from *Citizen Tom Paine* by Howard Fast

Howard Fast (1914–) has written several historical novels, including Spartacus *and* April Morning. *In* Citizen Tom Paine, *he tells the story of the Revolutionary war hero whose political pamphlets helped rally people to the American cause. Thomas Paine left England for America in 1774, published his famous pamphlet* Common Sense *soon after, and then joined up to fight for the Americans. The following passage takes place at a low point early in the war. The British under General Howe have gained control of New York City. General George Washington is trying to save as much of his army as he can by retreating across the Hudson River and southwest through New Jersey.*

Then the enemy crossed the Hudson, flanked them, and Greene had to take his garrison out of Fort Lee,[1] double-time, a panic-stricken crowd running down the road to Hackensack,[2] Washington leading them, Greene and old Israel Putnam[3] whipping them along, more panic at Hackensack when they tried to reorganize with the mob, and then the whole rabble plodding out of Hackensack on the road to Newark,[4] less than three thousand of them now; and they, with the five thousand stationed in Westchester[5] under Lee, were all that was left of the twenty thousand continentals[6] who had held New York. It rained and they dragged through the mud, whipped and miserable; they were starting a retreat that had no end in sight, and this was all that remained of the glorious revolution and the glorious army. In Newark they were jeered at by the Jersey citizens who were so sure they were seeing the last act of a miserable drama. They ran, fell, crawled, panted through the town, and scarcely were they out of one end than the British patrols entered the other.

Rain changed to the winter's first snow on the road to New Brunswick,[7] and marching through the slow-drifting flakes, they were a column of sorry and forlorn ghosts, muskets and rusty bayonets, here and there a cocked hat, a bandage, a cannon or two trundling clumsily, no sound and no song and no cheering, the officers walking their horses with faces bent against the cold. The road was bordered with stone walls, mantled in white now; the fields were dead and flat and the houses wore masks of shutters.

Paine walked beside a boy whose name was Clyde Matton, and who came from Maine. Carrying his own gun and the boy's, Paine had an arm around his thin shoulder. "The march is short," Paine said, "when one minds the road and not the steps."

"I reckon it's too long either way."

"There'll be a warm fire tonight."

"Little comfort in that. I'm thinking of going home."

"Home's a far way off. There're few men here, but good men."

He walked by the carts of the wounded and told them stories. They found him a

---

1. **Greene had to . . . Fort Lee:** General Nathanael Greene had to remove part of the Continental Army from Fort Lee in northeastern New Jersey.
2. **Hackensack:** a town (now a city) in northeastern New Jersey.
3. **Israel Putnam:** an older Revolutionary general.
4. **Newark:** a town (now a large city) further south in New Jersey.
5. **Westchester:** a New York county north of New York City.
6. **continentals:** soldiers in the Continental Army.
7. **New Brunswick:** a town (now a city) further southwest in New Jersey.

good story-teller; he could make things sound funny, and he was a fine mimic of accents. Already, he had picked up the vernacular of the various colonies, and he had a deadpan method of delivery, his heavy beaked nose inquiring for effect after each sentence. In spite of what he had gone through, he had never been healthier physically; his large, freckled face inspired confidence, and whether it was a cart mired in the muck or a man fainted from weariness, Paine's big shoulders and slab-like hands were ready and willing. Before this, strength had meant nothing, the power of mules and work-horses and slaves, but now it was something that gave him a heady[8] sort of happiness—as once, when remaining behind with Knox[9] and Alexander Hamilton[10] and a dozen others to hold a rear guard crossing with a gun, he had alone driven off a flanking attack of dragoons,[11] wading among the horses and sabers and flailing his big musket around his head like a light cane, taking nothing in return but a slight cut over the eye and a powder burn on the cheek. Telling about it admiringly, young Hamilton said:

"He's filthy and slovenly enough when you come to that, but he's the bravest man I ever saw, and he has the strength of a madman."

The bloodstains they left on the road where their bare feet dragged made him refuse Greene's offer of boots; he wasn't acting, but he was living the one life that was undeniably his own, this thing called revolution, learning a technique among this defeated, fleeing army, learning the one life he might live.

At night, they made their fires when they could not march a step more, and it was Paine to do the cooking for a hundred men, Paine to calm a boy's fear, Paine to read a man a letter from his wife and write one in return. Paine to sit with his strong hands clasped about his bent knees and slowly, simply explain what they were suffering for, the politics of an empire and a world, the struggles of mankind from the Romans to now, the new day of small men, not only in America but the world over.

The officers left him alone. He had hardly anything to do with them now, and they, in turn, realized that a dirty, unshaven English staymaker[12] was one of the few things that kept what was left of the American cause from dissolving into thin air.

Washington was not the man Paine had met in Philadelphia, not the long, carefully groomed Virginia aristocrat,[13] not the richest man in America and lord of Mt. Vernon,[14] but haggard and skinny, the face drawn, the light gray eyes bloodshot, the buff and blue uniform, for all its launderings, spotted with dirt-stains and bloodstains. Washington was a man who said to Paine:

"Whatever you can do—"

"It's little that I can do," Paine nodded. "If you mean write something, it's hard to tell a man who is suffering and giving that he must suffer more and give more."

"I don't know you," the Virginian said. "But there are so many things I don't know now I thought I knew once. I don't know how to put my faith in a staymaker, but I am doing it. I am glad to call you my friend, Paine, and I would be proud if you'd take my

---

8. heady: dizzy.

9. Knox: Henry Knox, a Revolutionary officer.

10. Alexander Hamilton: a Revolutionary officer.

11. dragoons (druh•GOONZ): heavily armed British troops.

12. staymaker: Paine's trade before leaving England. Stays are stiff strips of fabric used in corsets, collars, and cuffs.

13. aristocrat: a member of the noble class.

14. Mt. Vernon: George Washington's estate in Virginia.

hand, not as the writer of *Common Sense*, but as one man to another."

They shook hands, Paine with tears in his eyes.

"If you can write something," Washington said, "not only for the army but for the whole country. We're so near to the end—"

Paine was thinking he would die gladly for this man, die or kneel on the ground he walked.

Well, writing was what a writing man should do. With the drum held between his knees, with the top tilted to catch the wavering light of the fire, he scratched and scratched away, all the night through. The men gathered around him, men who knew Paine and loved him, men who had felt the strength of his arms, men who had slogged side by side with him. They read as he wrote, sometimes aloud in their stiff, nasal back-country accents:

"These are the times that try[15] men's souls. The summer soldier and the sunshine patriot will, in this crisis, shrink from the service of their country; but he that stands it now, deserves the love and thanks of man and woman. Tyranny, like hell, is not easily conquered. . . ."[16]

They read:

"If there be trouble, let it be in my day, that my child may have peace . . ."

With bloodshot eyes, they read and spoke softly:

"I call not upon a few, but upon all: not on this state or that state, but on every state: up and help us; lay your shoulders to the wheel; better have too much force than too little, when so great an object is at stake. Let it be told to the future world, that in the depth of winter, when nothing but hope and virtue could survive, that the city and the country, alarmed at one common danger, came forth to meet and repulse[17] it. . . ."

---

15. try: test.

16. These . . . conquered. . . . : The opening words of the first pamphlet in Paine's new Revolutionary pamphlet series *The American Crisis.*

17. repulse: to drive back.

Main Ideas

1. What is happening to Washington's Continental Army at this point in the war? What does Washington encourage Paine to do?

2. What observations does Paine make about General Washington?

Critical Thinking

3. **Drawing Conclusions** What do the details in the selection suggest about the Revolutionary troops and the ideals behind their cause?

4. **Recognizing Effects** What do the details suggest about the impact that Paine's writing had on the war effort?

Reteaching Activity

Making Inferences

Read each clue and answer the question "Who am I?" Write your answer in the blank.

1. I was a Jewish immigrant from Poland who spied on the British in New York in 1776.

   WHO AM I? _____

2. I was the first commander of the Continental Army and led my men to victory at Trenton and Princeton.

   WHO AM I? _____

3. I was nicknamed Molly Pitcher because I carried water to tired soldiers during a battle.

   WHO AM I? _____

4. I was the British General who arrived in New York in July, 1776, and later defeated the Americans at the Battle of Brandywine.

   WHO AM I? _____

5. I was the political writer who wrote a series called *The American Crisis.*

   WHO AM I? _____

6. Known by the nickname "Gentleman Johnny," I captured Fort Ticonderoga.

   WHO AM I? _____

7. I was the Mohawk chief who tried to convince the Iroquois to fight for the British.

   WHO AM I? _____

8. I was the American general who tricked the British at Fort Stanwix but later betrayed my country.

   WHO AM I? _____

9. I was in command of the Continental Army at Saratoga.

   WHO AM I? _____

10. I was the Polish engineer who designed fortifications to protect American soldiers at Bemis Heights.

    WHO AM I? _____

Reteaching Activity

Reading Comprehension

Choose the best answer for each item. Write the letter of your answer in the blank.

_____ 1. In 1779, Americans were receiving help from their allies
(a) England and France.
(b) France and Spain.
(c) France and Russia.

_____ 2. The victories of Bernardo de Gálvez prevented the British from attacking the United States from
(a) the northeast.
(b) the southwest.
(c) the Atlantic Ocean.

_____ 3. The Marquis de Lafayette was nicknamed
(a) "the soldier's friend."
(b) "the fearless Frenchman."
(c) "the noble soldier."

_____ 4. The German officer who trained Washington's army at Valley Forge was
(a) Baron de Kalb.
(b) Baron von Steuben.
(c) the Red Baron.

_____ 5. Valley Forge is remembered for its
(a) hot summer.
(b) wet and rainy spring.
(c) cold winter.

_____ 6. George Rogers Clark captured
(a) Fort Pitt.
(b) Fort Detroit.
(c) Fort Sackville.

_____ 7. A privately owned ship that has permission to attack enemy merchant vessels is called
(a) a privateer.
(b) a Forten.
(c) a submarine.

_____ 8. The American officer who declared "I have not yet begun to fight!" was
(a) Richard Bonhomme.
(b) John Paul Jones.
(c) Benjamin Franklin.

Reteaching Activity

Sequencing Events

Study the dates in the first column of the chart. In the second column, write the letter of the military event that occurred on that date. In the third column, write **B** if the British were victorious at this event. Write **A** if the Americans were victorious at this event.

  A. Battle of Camden

  B. Battle of Kings Mountain

  C. Battle of Yorktown

  D. Capture of Savannah

DATE	MILITARY EVENT	WINNER
1. December, 1778		
2. August, 1780		
3. October, 1780		
4. October, 1781		

Reteaching Activity

Analyzing Causes and Recognizing Effects

A. Listed below are four advantages the Americans had in the Revolutionary War. In the space that follows, explain how each advantage helped the Americans to defeat the British.

1. Better leadership

   _____

   _____

2. Foreign aid

   _____

   _____

3. Knowledge of the land

   _____

   _____

4. Motivation

   _____

   _____

B. Read the following statements about the United States after the Revolutionary War. Some of these things followed from the American victory in the Revolution. Others did not. In the blank before each item, write **T** if the statement is true and **F** if it is false.

_____   1. The United States became independent.

_____   2. The boundaries of the United States were the Mississippi River to the west, Canada to the north, and Spanish Florida to the south.

_____   3. Many Loyalists left the United States and moved to Canada.

_____   4. All adult men and women were given the right to vote.

_____   5. States began to abolish laws that discriminated against certain religions.

_____   6. Slavery was made illegal throughout the United States.

Chapter 7 Section 2 The War Expands

Enrichment Activity

Interviewing Soldiers

Activity With one or more classmates, interview soldiers who are spending the winter of 1777–1778 at Valley Forge. One person will act as the interviewer, while the others will be soldiers.

Strategies for Interviewing Interviews usually contain both direct and open-ended questions. An example of a direct question might be, "How long have you been here?" An open-ended question is more general, such as "What are the conditions at Valley Forge this winter?" Avoid questions that have a simple "yes" or "no" answer.

---

1. Preparing for the Interview

- **Gather information.** Your research may uncover stories about specific soldiers who can be the subjects for your interviews. Students being interviewed must also do thorough research.

- **Formulate your questions.** Try to find questions that will encourage your interviewee to tell an interesting story.

- **Decide if you want to tape the final interview.** Audio- or videotaped interviews can be played back for your own class or for future classes.

2. Practicing the Interview

- **Be flexible with your questions.** Listen carefully to the soldier's responses to see if a follow-up question is needed.

- **Stay on the point.** If the soldier you're interviewing strays to a different subject, politely remind him or her of the question you asked.

- **Take good notes or record the interview.** Notes or a tape recording will help you draft a final list of questions for presenting the interview.

- **Write an introduction and conclusion.** When you present the interview(s), you will want to set the scene beforehand and wrap it up afterwards.

3. Presenting the Interview

- **Present your interview.** Either conduct your interview "live" in front of the class or play a tape recording of it.

Reflect and Assess

At the end of the interview, discuss the process you followed. Explore the ideas and issues below.

- What was the most difficult part of conducting the interview?

- Ask the class whether they learned anything new about the difficult conditions soldiers faced at Valley Forge.

- Who do you think is most responsible for an interesting, informative interview, the interviewer or the person being interviewed?

Chapter **8** *Confederation to Constitution*

Setting the Stage

Reading Strategy: Solving Problems

Many teenagers today are actively involved in solving their communities' problems. These young people carry out plans to make their communities better places. **Solving problems** refers to the course of action taken to improve or correct a difficult situation.

In Chapter 8, Americans are faced with challenging problems. The chart below identifies four major ones. How will these problems be solved? As you read the chapter, fill in the chart with the solutions.

Problems	Solutions
Western lands	1.
Postwar depression	2.
Representation in the new government	3.
Slavery	4.

Discussion Questions

1. Which solution on your chart was a great achievement of the Confederation Congress? Why?

2. Which problem on your chart caused Massachusetts farmers to rebel? Explain.

3. Which solutions on your chart became part of the Constitution? Explain.

Chapter **8** Confederation to Constitution

Tracing Themes

Theme: Democratic Ideals	Chapter Connection
Individuals in a democratic society have basic rights. The institutions that protect and extend those rights are a critical part of American history.	To remedy the weaknesses of the Articles of Confederation, the nation's leaders created the Constitution. This document established the framework for stable, democratic government in the United States.

Tracing Themes Through U.S. History
The creation of laws and institutions to ensure democratic rights is a tradition in American life. For example, in Chapter 18 amendments to the Constitution during the Reconstruction era guarantee certain rights to millions of freed African Americans.

Critical Thinking Activity

Create a diagram like the one shown below. In the labeled areas, list the main features of the Articles of Confederation and the Constitution. In the middle, list the democratic principles the two documents shared. After completing the diagram, answer the critical thinking questions.

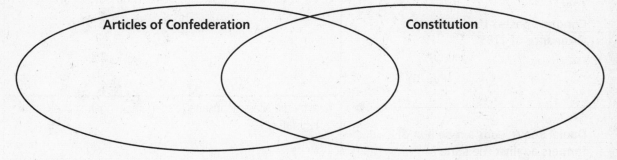

1. **Drawing Conclusions**   Why did the Articles of Confederation appeal to Americans with strong democratic ideals?

   _____

   _____

2. **Forming and Supporting Opinions**   One of the problems faced in writing the Constitution was balancing the interests of small and large states in the national legislature. Describe the problem and explain how it was solved. Was this a good solution?

   _____

3. **Making Decisions**   Would you have voted to ratify the Constitution without the promise of a Bill of Rights? Why, or why not?

   _____

Chapter **8** *Section 1 The Confederation Era*

Guided Reading

Sequencing Events As you read this section, answer the questions about the events shown on the time line below.

1775

1775
Daniel Boone leads settlers into Kentucky and helps build the Wilderness Road.

1. What did the American settlers find when they reached Kentucky?

1781
The Articles of Confederation take effect.

2. Why did the Articles of Confederation not take effect until 1781?

1785
Congress passes the Land Ordinance of 1785.

3. What did the Land Ordinance of 1785 do?

1787
Daniel Shays leads a rebellion of farmers against the state legislature in Massachusetts.

4. Why did Masssachusetts farmers rebel against their state legislature?

1787
Congress passes the Northwest Ordinance.

5. How was the Northwest Ordinance different than the Land Ordinance of 1785?

Chapter **8** *Section 2 Creating the Constitution*

Guided Reading

A. Making Generalizations As you read the section, take notes on the characteristics of the people who served as delegates to the Convention.

Characteristic	Characteristic

Generalization

Characteristic	Characteristic

B. Summarizing Use the chart below to summarize the Virginia Plan and the New Jersey Plan.

1. The Virginia Plan proposed a legislature that consisted of:	2. The New Jersey Plan proposed a legislature that consisted of:
3. Who supported the Virginia Plan?	4. Who supported the New Jersey Plan?
5. How did the Great Compromise settle this issue?	

C. Analyzing Points of View On the back of this paper, briefly explain the disagreement between Northerners and Southerners that was settled by the Three-Fifths Compromise.

Chapter **8** *Section 3 Ratifying the Constitution*

Guided Reading

A. Analyzing Points of View As you read the section, take notes on the people and ideas involved in the debate over ratification of the Constitution.

1. What were the Federalists?	2. What were the Antifederalists?
3. Who were the leading Federalists?	4. Who were the leading Antifederalists?
5. What reasons did the Federalists give to defend their views on the ratification?	6. What reasons did the Antifederalists give to defend their views on the Constitution?

B. Summarizing On the back of this paper, summarize the arguments in favor of adding a bill of rights to the Constitution.

Building Vocabulary

Antifederalists	Federalists	Northwest Territory
Articles of Confederation	Great Compromise	republic
Bill of Rights	James Madison	Shays's Rebellion
Constitutional Convention	New Jersey Plan	Three-Fifths Compromise
federalism	Northwest Ordinance	Virginia Plan

A. Completion Select the term or name that best completes the sentence.

Support for strengthening the national government increased after

(1) _____ broke out in Massachusetts in 1786. At the Constitutional

Convention the following spring, one of the leaders was (2) _____.

He and others established a (3) _____, a country in which the people

choose representatives to govern them. The Constitution was based on

(4) _____, a system of government in which power is shared among

the central government and the states. Helping to protect citizens from the powers

of the national government is the (5) _____.

B. Matching Match the definition in the second column with the word in the first column.
Write the appropriate letter next to the word.

_____ 1. Wilderness Road   a. an act on surveying western territories

_____ 2. Land Ordinance of 1785   b. a proposal for a one-house legislature

_____ 3. Northwest Territory   c. a set of essays defending the Constitution

_____ 4. Northwest Ordinance   d. a trail into Kentucky

_____ 5. Virginia Plan   e. an agreement on how to count the slave
                       population when setting taxes

_____ 6. New Jersey Plan

_____ 7. Great Compromise   f. an act on governing western territories

_____ 8. Three-Fifths Compromise   g. an agreement on legislative representation

_____ 9. *The Federalist* papers   h. a Virginian who opposed the Constitution

_____ 10. George Mason   i. the region from Ohio through Wisconsin

                       j. a proposal for a two-house legislature

C. Writing Use each of the following terms correctly in a paragraph on how to divide power under
federalism. Underline each word you use.

Articles of Confederation	Constitutional Convention	James Madison
Federalists	Antifederalists	

Chapter **8** *Section 3 Ratifying the Constitution*

Skillbuilder Practice
Analyzing Points of View

People often have conflicting points of view on political issues. Virginia's leaders were closely divided over support for the proposed Constitution. **Analyze the points of view** of two influential Virginians, Patrick Henry and Edmund Pendleton. Then fill in the chart below. Some answers have been provided. (See Skillbuilder Handbook, page R9.)

Patrick Henry

I have the highest [respect] for those gentlemen [who wrote the Constitution]; but, sir, give me leave to demand—What right had they to say, "We, the people"? My political curiosity . . . leads me to ask—Who authorized them to speak the language of "We, the people," instead of, "We, the states"? States are the characteristics and soul of a confederation. If the states be not the agents of this compact, it must be one great, consolidated, national government of the people of all the states.

Edmund Pendleton

But an objection is made to the form: the expression "We the people" is thought improper. Permit me to ask the gentleman who made this objection, who but the people can delegate powers? Who but the people have a right to form government? . . . If the objection be that the Union ought to be not of the people but of the state governments, then I think the choice of the former very happy and proper. What have the state governments to do with it? Were they to determine, the people would not, in that case, be the judges upon what terms it was adopted.

Annals of America (Chicago: Encyclopaedia Britannica, 1968) Volume III, 280–287.

	Henry's Point of View	Pendleton's Point of View
1. How does the writer view the phrase "We the people"?	Doesn't like the phrase. The government should be established by the states.	
2. Summarize the writer's main concern.	Wants the states to make the decisions	
3. State the writer's general view of the proposed Constitution.	Opposed ratification	

Name _____   Date _____

Geography Application
Ratifying the Constitution

Delegates to the Constitutional Convention in Philadelphia signed their approval of the document on September 17, 1787. Yet the proposed Constitution was controversial.

The Constitution said that 9 (of the 13) states were needed to ratify the Constitution. Reaching that number would not be easy. One state, Rhode Island, had protested the idea of a national government from the beginning. It had not even sent delegates to the convention. Then, some states feared that the Constitution would take away too much of their power. Others feared that it would allow larger states to dominate. Some Southern states distrusted Northern states.

People formed two groups. Antifederalists opposed the Constitution. This included a great number of people who were small farmers and lived in rural areas. Federalists supported it. This included the majority of people who owned large properties and businesses. People who lived in larger towns also generally supported it. The map below details how the states were split on ratification.

Congress moved ahead. On September 28, it sent the Constitution to the 13 states for approval. At the same time Congress called for special ratifying conventions in each state. This move bypassed some state legislatures that opposed the document. Eventually all state conventions approved the Constitution. Rhode Island was last, taking nearly three years.

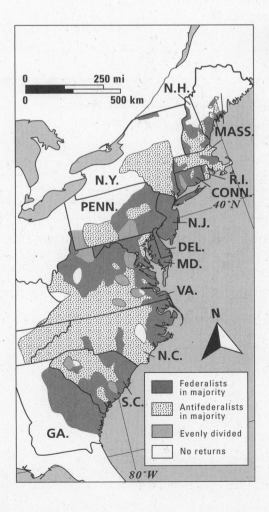

Percentage of Votes For and Against Ratification of the Constitution		
State	**% For**	**% Against**
Delaware	100	0
Georgia	100	0
New Jersey	100	0
Maryland	85	15
Connecticut	76	24
North Carolina	72	28
Pennsylvania	67	33
South Carolina	67	33
New Hampshire	55	45
Massachusetts	53	47
New York	53	47
Virginia	53	47
Rhode Island	52	48

Interpreting Maps and Text

1. Which three states supported only the Federalist pro-ratification position?

_____

2. Georgia was 100 percent in favor of ratifying the Constitution. Yet unlike New Jersey and Delaware, the state is not completely covered by "Federalists in majority" patterning. Explain how this could be.

_____

_____

_____

3. Which position won more support in coastal areas (where the biggest towns were located)?

_____

4. Where was Antifederalist support concentrated?

_____

_____

5. Look at the pattern for New York. Antifederalists controlled most of the state's territory. Why do you suppose that support for ratification won out?

_____

_____

_____

6. Why is it not surprising that Rhode Island's vote total was the closest?

_____

_____

_____

7. Consider the map again. What would have happened if New York alone had failed to vote for ratification?

_____

_____

_____

Primary Source
A Letter from Benjamin Lincoln

The outbreak of Shays's Rebellion worried many people, including George Washington. From his home in Virginia, Washington wrote to his friend General Benjamin Lincoln, asking about the event. Lincoln was in charge of the Massachusetts militia that would be sent to stop the rebellion. Below is part of Lincoln's response to Washington, dated December 4, 1786.

I cannot . . . be surprised to hear your Excellency inquire, "Are your people getting mad? Are we to have the goodly fabric, that eight years were spent in raising, pulled over our heads? What is the cause of all these commotions? When and how will they end?" . . . I will make some observations which shall involve in them the best answers to the several questions in my power to give.

"Are your people getting mad?" Many of them appear to be absolutely so, if an attempt to annihilate our present constitution and dissolve the present government can be considered as evidences of insanity.

"Are we to have the goodly fabric, that eight years were spent in rearing, pulled over our heads?" There is great danger that it will be so, I think, unless the tottering system shall be supported by arms, and even then a government which has no other basis than the point of the bayonet . . . is so totally different from the one established, . . . it can hardly be said that we have supported "the goodly fabric." . . .

"What is the cause of all these commotions?" The causes are too many and too various for me to pretend to trace and point them out. I shall therefore only mention some of those which appear to be the principal ones. Among those I may rank the ease with which property was acquired, with which credit was obtained, and debts were discharged, in the time of war. Hence people were diverted from their usual industry[1] and economy.[2] A luxuriant mode of living crept into vogue,[3] and soon that income, by which the expenses of all should as much as possible be limited, was no long considered as having anything to do with the question at what expense families ought to live, or rather which they ought not to have exceeded. . . .

It is impossible for me to determine "when and how they will end"; as I see little probability that they will be brought to a period, and the dignity of government supported, without bloodshed. . . . The proportion of debtors run high in this State. Too many of them are against the government. The men of property and the holders of the public securities are generally supporters of our present constitution. Few of these men have been in the field, and it remains quite problematical whether they will in time so fully discover their own interests as they shall be induced thereby to lend for a season part of their property for the security of the remainder. If these classes of men should not turn out on the broad scale with spirit, . . . our constitution will be overturned.

from A. B. Hart, ed., *American History Told By Contemporaries*, Vol. 3 (New York, 1986). Reprinted in *Voices from America's Past* Vol. 1, ed. by Richard B. Morris and James Woodress (New York: E. P. Dutton, 1963), 146–148.

1. **industry:** hard work.
2. **economy:** thrift.
3. **vogue:** fashion.

Main Ideas

1. What does Lincoln say is the main cause of the unrest?

2. Who does Lincoln blame for the unrest?

Critical Thinking

3. **Identifying Facts and Opinions** Who does Lincoln suggest could prevent the rebels from overturning the government?

4. **Making Inferences** Do you think Lincoln is on the side of the rebels?

Primary Source

from *Debates on the Adoption of the Federal Constitution*

Benjamin Franklin was one of the oldest delegates at the Constitutional Convention in 1787. He had a reputation for wisdom. He used his influence to remind the younger men of the importance of compromise. The following speech is one of his most important. Franklin delivered it near the end of the convention. James Madison wrote it down as it was read.

The engrossed[1] Constitution being read, Dr. Franklin rose with a speech in his hand, which he had reduced to writing for his own convenience, and which Mr. Wilson read in the words following:

"Mr. President: I confess that there are several parts of this Constitution which I do not at present approve, but I am not sure I shall never approve them. For, having lived long, I have experienced many instances of being obliged, by better information or fuller consideration, to change opinions, even on important subjects, which I once thought right, but found to be otherwise. It is therefore that, the older I grow, the more apt I am to doubt my own judgment, and to pay more respect to the judgment of others. . . . But though many private persons think almost as highly of their own infallibility[2] as of that of their sect,[3] few express it so naturally as a certain French lady, who, in a dispute with her sister, said, 'I don't know how it happens, sister, but I meet with nobody but myself that is always in the right.' . . .

"In these sentiments, sir, I agree to this Constitution, with all its faults, if they are such; because I think a general government necessary for us, and there is no form of government, but what may be a blessing to the people if well administered; and believe further, that this is likely to be well administered for a course of years, and can only end in despotism,[4] as other forms have done before it, when the people shall become so corrupted as to need despotic government, being incapable of any other. . . . Thus I consent, sir, to this Constitution, because I expect no better, and because I am not sure, that it is not the best. The opinions I have had of its errors I sacrifice to the public good. I have never whispered a syllable of them abroad. Within these walls they were born, and here they shall die. . . .

"On the whole, sir, I cannot help expressing a wish that every member of the Convention, who may still have objections to it, would with me, on this occasion, doubt a little of his own infallibility, and, to make manifest[5] our unanimity, put his name to this instrument." He then moved that the Constitution be signed by the members.

from *Debates on the Adoption of the Federal Constitution,* ed. by Jonathan Elliot (Philadelphia, 1861). Reprinted in *Eyewitness to America,* ed. by David Colbert (New York: Pantheon Books, 1997), 100–103.

1. **engrossed:** clean version of a document.
2. **infallibility:** incapable of error.
3. **sect:** a religious group.
4. **despotism:** rule by a tyrant.
5. **manifest:** clear for everyone to see.

Main Ideas

1. What is Franklin's opinion of the proposed Constitution?

2. What is Franklin urging the members of the convention to do?

Critical Thinking

3. **Analyzing Points of View** What point is Franklin making with the comment about the French lady?

4. **Drawing Conclusions** What is Franklin's point when he says that "there is no form of government, but what may be a blessing to the people if well adminstered?"

Literature Selection

from *Our Independence and the Constitution* by Dorothy Canfield Fisher

Dorothy Canfield Fisher (1879–1958) was a famous educator. She also wrote many books, both fiction and nonfiction. In Our Independence and the Constitution, *she combines the two forms, recounting actual historical events from the viewpoint of a fictional young girl named Debby, who lives in Philadelphia. The following excerpt takes place in 1787, when delegates begin to gather in Philadelphia for the Constitutional Convention.*

The Americans had won the war against Great Britain, yes. But what it had cost them!

The trouble was that they hadn't learned how to stick together. Yet they couldn't get along if they didn't.

The trouble with the old way of sticking together, which just hadn't worked at all, was that it had been rushed through at the very time the Americans had been at war with England. They couldn't possibly fight the war, each State by itself. So in a great hurry, just because they had to, they had made an agreement to work together. This agreement was called the *Articles of Confederation.*

It hadn't worked well during the war, and it was hardly working at all now. Yet more than ever, the States needed to agree with each other. Everywhere in America, many people were scared to think how helpless their own State would be, by itself, if it were attacked by a big, rich European country with a fine army and navy. And it was not only the great danger from outside. Inside the country there was already a lot of jealousy between the different States. Some of them were beginning to act as though there were no American Confederation left at all, as if they were all separate countries.

If they were separate countries, they would have differences of opinion, and every time this happened they'd go to war with each other, to get their own way. That was the way the different European countries had always acted—fighting each other at the drop of a hat, century after century. And look what they had lost in money, deaths, poverty and misery!

There *must* be some way of getting together that would work better than fighting each other. That's what the Convention of 1787 in Philadelphia was to be for: to invent a new set of rules (a Constitution) to make that much-needed central government strong enough to do the things the States desperately needed and which they couldn't do, each one by itself.

Inside Debby's home there was not one new thing—except Debby. She was now a slim, long-legged fifteen-year-old girl—as tall as her mother. You'd never have known her for the chubby little chunk who had played in the sand-pile. It was a very happy home, full of love and fun; but everything except Debby was worn out and threadbare. Her mother's hair was gray, although she was only forty-six years old. Her father's was quite white at fifty. He had to have crutches to walk, because his left leg had been cut off. It had been frozen that dreadful winter the American army had spent at Valley Forge, with mighty little to eat, and thin ragged old coats and, even with deep snow on the ground, hardly any shoes at all.

The line of march of those American soldiers was red with blood from their bruised and bleeding feet. Yet their country was not so poor that it could not buy shoes for its own soldiers. The reason was a legal one. The Articles of Confederation—that first set of hastily invented rules—didn't provide any way for the Continental Congress to get taxes which would have brought in enough money from the States to buy new clothes and shoes and decent food for the American soldiers.

So Debby's father lost a leg for lack of the right kind of Constitution. He had a job now in the post office. It was work at a desk, work a veteran could do, even with one leg gone. The family had breakfast early, so that he would have time to hobble downtown on his crutches. . . .

There was money, of course. He had a salary. But it was paid by the United States government. So his pay was in paper money. "Continental Currency" it was called, and that was worth just exactly nothing. Or almost. The Continental Congress hadn't had any legal power to make the States pay their fair share of the nation's expenses. Then, too, during the war there was so much confusion and uncertainty, and the States were so poor, that most of them paid very little. So the Continental Congress had to go on printing paper money. The more they printed, the less it would buy. People with things to sell were afraid it would be worth even less tomorrow than today. So they ran up the prices of food and clothing to be on the safe side.

If it hadn't been for the two boys, Debby's family would hardly have known how to manage at all. They were grown-up men of twenty-five and twenty-three now. The older one, like his father, had been in the American Army, and one winter had camped out in Chester County, not far from Philadelphia. There he had met a farmer's family, and—to make the story short—had gone back after the American victory which ended that long terrible war for Independence, and married the farmer's daughter. They had a little boy now. So Debby was "Aunt Deborah"—quite a change.

The farm was a fine one, on rich, deep, fertile soil. Americans were lucky in those hard days if somebody in the family lived on a farm! Once in so often the Chester County family would hitch up their two horses to the farm wagon, and drive in to visit the "old folks" in Philadelphia. They always brought presents from the farm. Sometimes it was a couple of fleeces[1] from their sheep. Out of this wool Debby and her mother made homespun cloth for their menfolks' coats and breeches[2] and their own winter dresses. Or they knitted stockings and coats and underwear and even winter nightgowns and nightcaps. Or they used that homespun thread for the endless darning and mending. Everything in the house was wearing out, rugs, wraps, underwear.

As for food, they used every inch of their back garden to grow vegetables. Years ago, there had been, so Debby's parents told her, a flower garden and a grass plot, where on summer evenings they often sat out under the pear tree. Now the pear tree stood in the middle of a small field, where peas and beans and squash and pumpkins and corn grew right up to the back door. Debby and her mother worked there, with her father, to raise food. Everybody on their street was raising food like this. The younger people couldn't remember when they didn't.

They went without a good many things—including anything new for the house. No, there *was* one new thing. A big framed picture of General George Washington.

---

1. fleeces: coats of wool from sheep.

2. breeches: trousers that extend to just below the knee.

This hung over the mantelpiece. Debby couldn't remember when it had not hung there. But one day when she was cleaning the attic, her older brother was up with her. He found another framed picture, face down, under the eaves. Debby had never noticed it. He pulled it out, stood it up, wiped off some of the dust from it, and gazed at it a long time.

"Who is that?" asked Debby, leaning on a broom, her head tied up in a dusting cloth, looking over his shoulder. "A man with a fat face like that shouldn't wear such a high collar."

Her brother was astonished. "Don't you *know*?" he cried out.

She looked again. "No. Should I?"

Her brother saw that she really didn't recognize the face. "Well, you *are* an American girl!" he exclaimed. "That's King George III. It used to hang in our living room, just where General Washington's picture now is. Think of your not even remembering."

"Oh, I was only four years old," said Debby. "How could I?"

She went on sweeping, cautiously, not to raise too much dust. Her brother set the picture up and gazed at it. "It takes me back!" he murmured. "I remember so well the day when Mother took it down." To his sister he said, "Do you know, our brother told me that the last time his ship was in an English port, Bristol, I think it was, everybody there was gossiping about the King's going crazy. Really crazy, you know. Insane. People were saying he'd soon have to be locked up or put into a strait-jacket,[3] to keep him from attacking the people around him."

Debby had no comment to make on this. She did not care a bit what happened to a king. Why should she? She was an American, and if there was one thing you could be sure of with any young American, it was that he wasn't interested in kings. Their parents sometimes talked about the King. When they did, they got angry. . . . They were always getting excited about something or other. For people of Debby's age, kings were already far in the past. . . . It sounded like "history talk," to her, although it happened only eleven years ago.

But it did not seem to her the least bit like "history talk" when people discussed and argued and hoped about getting a Constitution that would be better than the agreement the States had hastily scrambled together in war times. Debby saw the need for that. Anybody with an eye in his head understood that if the States could really act together and support a central government, it would mean something. If they got some rules made about taxes paid to the government that would give her father his salary in good hard money—that would not be "history," that would be news.

---

3. **strait-jacket:** a garment that holds the arms of a violent person tightly against the body.

Main Ideas

1. According to the passage, what is wrong with the Articles of Confederation?

2. Why doesn't Debby care about the king?

Critical Thinking

3. **Evaluating** Why is jealousy among the states a dangerous thing? Explain.

4. **Recognizing Effects** How do the weaknesses of the government affect Debby's family?

Chapter **8** *Section 1 The Confederation Era*

Reteaching Activity

Evaluating

Write **T** in the blank if the statement is true. If the statement is false, write **F** in the blank and then write the corrected statement on the line below.

_____ 1. In the late 1700s, the main road into Kentucky was called Boone's Road.

_____

_____ 2. In a republic, people choose representatives to govern for them.

_____

_____ 3. The Articles of Confederation gave the national government the power to set taxes and enforce the law.

_____

_____ 4. Some smaller states would not ratify the Articles of Confederation until all states gave up their claims to Western lands.

_____

_____ 5. The Land Ordinance of 1785 described how the Northwest Territory was to be governed.

_____

_____ 6. Debt from the Revolutionary War was a major problem for the new United States government.

_____

_____ 7. In 1787, Daniel Shays led a rebellion of farmers who demanded debt relief.

_____

Name _____ Date _____

Reteaching Activity

Reading Comprehension

Use the list of words below to fill in the blanks in the paragraphs that follow.

Constitution	executive	Great	New Jersey
Philadelphia	ratification	Senate	slave trade
slaves	Three-Fifths	Virginia	George Washington

In the summer of 1787, representatives of 12 states met in (1) _____ for the Constitutional Convention. The delegates elected (2) _____ as president for the convention.

Edmund Randolph offered the (3) _____ Plan. This plan proposed that government should consist of a legislative branch, an (4) _____ branch, and a judicial branch. The legislature would have two houses with the power to tax, regulate commerce, and make laws. The number of representatives in each house would be based on a state's population or wealth.

As an alternative, William Paterson proposed the (5) _____ Plan. This called for a legislature with one house. The legislature would have the power to regulate trade and to tax foreign goods. Each state would receive one vote in this legislature.

Most delegates liked the Virginia Plan better but did not agree on how to determine representation. A committee was selected to solve the disagreement. The solution was called the (6) _____ Compromise. In one house of the legislature, each state would have an equal number of votes. This house was called the (7) _____ . In the other house of the legislature, representation would be based on each state's population. This house was called the House of Representatives.

To decide the number of representatives in the House of Representatives, delegates had to agree on who should be counted. Southern states contained many more (8) _____ than Northern states. Southern states wanted to count these people for representation but not for taxation. Northern states wanted to count these people for taxation but not for representation. The solution agreed to was the (9) _____ Compromise.

The Convention also decided to delay banning the (10) _____ until 1808. Delegates did, however, agree to tax this form of commerce.

In September, the Convention voted for and wrote down the (11) _____ . All but three delegates signed the finished copy. This document was then sent to the Confederation Congress and on to the states for (12) _____ .

Reteaching Activity

Categorizing

A. Read the names below. Write **A** in the blank if the person was an Antifederalist and opposed to the Constitution. Write **F** in the blank if the person was a Federalist and supported the Constitution.

_____ 1. Alexander Hamilton

_____ 2. Patrick Henry

_____ 3. John Jay

_____ 4. James Madison

_____ 5. George Mason

Sequencing

B. Number the events below in the order in which they happened.

_____ 1. Connecticut and Georgia ratify the Constitution.

_____ 2. Delaware, New Jersey, and Pennsylvania ratify the Constitution.

_____ 3. Massachusetts ratifies the Constitution.

_____ 4. New York ratifies the Constitution.

_____ 5. North Carolina ratifies the Constitution.

_____ 6. Rhode Island ratifies the Constitution.

_____ 7. Virginia ratifies the Bill of Rights.

_____ 8. Virginia ratifies the Constitution.

Name _____   Date _____

 Chapter **8** *Section 3 Ratifying the Constitution*

Enrichment Activity

Point-Counterpoint: A Bill of Rights Issue

Activity With a partner, stage a mini-debate called a point-counterpoint on a Bill of Rights issue. You will argue one side of the issue while your partner argues the other. Each argument will consist of a three-minute speech.

Strategies for a Point-Counterpoint First, pick an issue about which you feel strongly. In order to convince others to agree with you, you will need to provide strong supporting evidence, or examples, for your argument. You will also need to anticipate and counter your opponent's arguments.

---

1. Organizing for the Point-Counterpoint

- **Choose your issue.** You may argue whether or not Congress should pass a flag burning amendment, whether or not gun control laws should be strengthened, or some other topic related to one of the first ten amendments.

- **Take a stand.** Decide which side of the issue appeals to you.

- **Research the issue.** Find facts, examples, statistics, and expert opinions that support each side. You can find information at your school or local library or on the Internet.

- **Order your ideas.** Decide whether you want to argue your strongest point first or whether you prefer to build your arguments toward a strong conclusion. Remember to include your opponent's likely arguments and your own counter arguments.

---

2. Preparing your speech

- **Write a rough draft.** To make your speech persuasive, use strong words like "must," "should," "never," and "always." Also, use persuasive techniques such as repetition—repeating your main point many times but with different wording. Write your speech on note cards to serve as a guide during the debate.

- **Practice delivering your speech.** You and your opponent will each have three minutes to present the speech. Make sure that you fall within these time guidelines.

---

3. Conducting the Point-Counterpoint

- **Decide who speaks first.** You can choose by having someone toss a coin.

- **Present your case.** Speak firmly and make eye contact with your audience.

- **Pay attention to your opponent.** Listen to the opposite point of view without interrupting.

---

4. Determining the most convincing speech.

- Ask your classmates to vote for or against the issue you and your opponent were debating.

Reflect and Assess

At the end of the point-counterpoint, discuss with your class the process you followed and the conclusions you reached. Explore the ideas and issues below.

- Did both speakers use enough information and examples to support their points of view?

- Did each speaker anticipate the other's arguments and counter them effectively?

- Which of the speakers' techniques did you find most effective?

Constitution Handbook   *Preamble and Article 1*

Guided Reading

A. Finding Main Ideas As you read the Preamble, fill in the cluster diagram with the six goals of the Constitution.

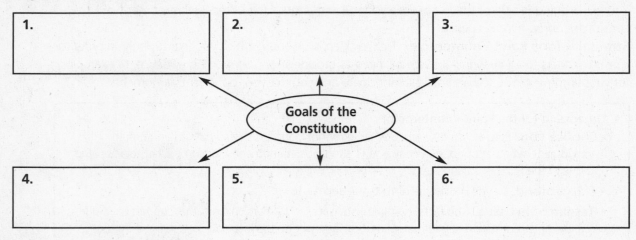

1.	2.	3.

Goals of the Constitution

4.	5.	6.

B. Comparing and Contrasting As you read about Congress in Article 1, fill in the chart with information about the House of Representatives and the Senate.

	House of Representatives	Senate
1. Candidates' requirements		
2. Term of office		
3. Number of members per state		
4. Impeachment		
5. Bills for raising money		
6. Military powers		
7. Role of vice president		

Constitution Handbook   *Articles 2 and 3*

Guided Reading

A. Summarizing As you read Article 2, fill in the diagram with examples of the president's powers and duties.

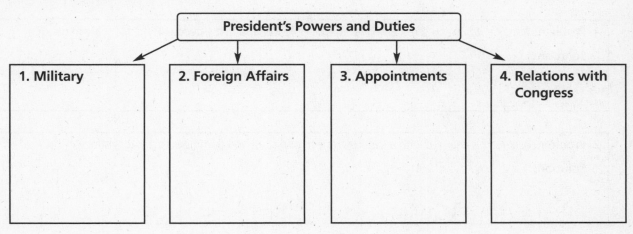

President's Powers and Duties

1. Military	2. Foreign Affairs	3. Appointments	4. Relations with Congress

B. Finding Main Ideas As you read Article 3, fill out the chart below with important information about the judicial branch of government.

1. What courts make up the judicial branch of government?

2. What is the term of office for a Supreme Court judge?

3. What is judicial power? Give two examples.

4. What "check," or control, does the Supreme Court have on Congress? Explain.

5. How does the Constitution define *treason*? What must happen before a person is convicted of treason?

Constitution Handbook   *Articles 4–7*

Guided Reading

A. Solving Problems As you read Article 4, explain how the Constitution solves each problem listed below.

---

1. Problem: A major U.S. city is the scene of domestic violence, and many people in the state are in danger.

Solution:

---

2. Problem: A person is charged with a serious crime in one state and then flees to another state.

Solution:

B. Summarizing As you read Article 5, explain the procedures for amending the Constitution.

1. Proposing Amendments	2. Ratifying Amendments

C. Summarizing As you read Article 6, complete the diagram below to show the bases for the "supreme law of the land."

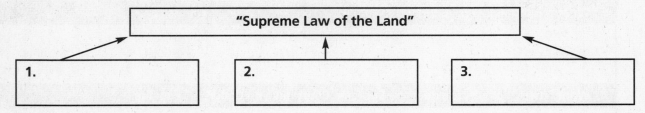

"Supreme Law of the Land"

1.

2.

3.

D. Finding Main Ideas As you read Article 7, answer the following questions.
1. How many states had to ratify the Constitution before it could go into effect?

_____

2. In what year was the Constitution signed by the delegates to the Constitutional Convention? _____

Constitution Handbook   The Bill of Rights and Amendments 11–27

Guided Reading

Categorizing As you read Amendments 1–27, fill in the chart below with a brief explanation of each amendment. Use the groupings shown as a guide.

Explanation

	Explanation
Personal Freedom Amendment 1 Amendment 2 Amendment 3 Amendment 4	
Fair Legal Treatment Amendment 5 Amendment 6 Amendment 7 Amendment 8	
Reserved Powers Amendment 9 Amendment 10	
Election Procedures and Conditions of Office Amendment 12 Amendment 17 Amendment 20 Amendment 22 Amendment 25 Amendment 27	
Social and Economic Changes Amendment 11 Amendment 13 Amendment 14 Amendment 16 Amendment 18 Amendment 21	
Voting Rights Amendment 15 Amendment 19 Amendment 23 Amendment 24 Amendment 26	

Answer Key

Setting the Stage

Reading Strategy
Possible Responses
1. Proclamation Act of 1763
2. Stamp Act, 1765
3. Declaratory Act, 1766
4. Townshend Acts, 1767
5. Boston Massacre, 1770
6. Tea Act, 1773
7. Boston Tea Party, 1773
8. Intolerable Acts, 1774
9. First Continental Congress, 1774
10. Battles at Lexington and Concord, 1775
11. Second Continental Congress, 1775
12. Declaration of Independence, 1776

Discussion Questions
Possible Responses
1. British actions—Proclamation Act of 1763, Stamp Act, Declaratory Act, Townshend Acts, Tea Act, Intolerable Acts, battles at Lexington and Concord Colonists' actions—Boston Massacre, Boston Tea Party, First Continental Congress, battles at Lexington and Concord, Second Continental Congress, Declaration of Independence
2. Tea Act and Boston Tea Party; Second Continental Congress and the Declaration of Independence
3. Most students will choose the Declaration of Independence.

Tracing Themes

Chart Answers
Samuel Adams—leads the Boston Sons of Liberty
Abigail Adams—writes insightful letters about revolutionary times
Thomas Paine—writes *Common Sense*
Phillis Wheatley—writes inspiring poetry about the patriotic cause and enslaved African Americans' struggle for freedom
1. It contains language that is vivid, emotional, and easy to understand.
2. Samuel Adams—relied on active resistance and organized groups to spread the protest movement against British policies; Thomas Jefferson—used writing to express the cause of independence
3. Answers will vary but should be supported with reasons.

Guided Reading

Section 1
A. Possible Responses
Britain's Solutions:
1. Proclamation Act (1763)—Stopped colonists from settling west of the Appalachian Mountains
2. Quartering Act of (1765)—Required colonists to house British soldiers and provide them with supplies
3. Sugar Act (1764)—Placed a tax on sugar, molasses, and other products shipped to the colonies
   Stamp Act (1765)—Placed a tax on all legal and commercial documents
4. Declaratory Act (1766)—Declared Parliament's supreme authority to govern the colonies
Colonists' Responses:
1. resentment; defiance of the act
2. anger
3. Sugar Act: anger; protests—"taxation without representation"
   Stamp Act: protests; boycott of British goods; creation of Sons of Liberty
4. power struggle with Parliament
B. Possible Responses
Patrick Henry—called for resistance to the Stamp Tax
boycott—organized by colonial merchants to protest the Stamp Act
Sons of Liberty—staged protests against the Stamp Act

Section 2
A. Possible Responses
1. taxes
   Townshend Acts
   writs of assistance
   threat to rights and freedoms
2. boycotts
   Sons of Liberty's protests
   Daughters of Liberty's call for homespun cloth
   peaceful demonstrations
   rioters
B. Possible Responses
1. Causes—Townshend Acts and other taxes; activities of the Sons of Liberty
   Effects—five colonists killed; trial of British soldiers arrested for murder; anti-British propaganda campaign
2. Causes—Parliament's push to raise money; control over American tea trade; Parliament's efforts to raise money.
   Effects—widespread protests; Boston Tea Party

Answer Key

C. Possible Responses
1. The Boston Tea Party was a just protest; the Boston Tea Party was an unjust protest.
2. approval—a. harsh measures needed to defy British tax policies; b. destruction of property, not people; c. show of colonial strength. Disapproval—destruction of property too extreme; nonviolent tactics best way to settle debate over taxes; show of disloyalty to Britain

Section 3
A. Possible Responses
1. Intolerable Acts—series of Parliament's harsh laws, such as closing Boston Harbor until colonists paid for destroyed tea and banning the committees of correspondence
2. banning trade with Britain until the repeal of the Intolerable Acts; training troops in each colony
3. colonial troops prepared to fight at a minute's notice
4. to capture Samuel Adams and John Hancock and to destroy American supplies
5. signaled the start of the American Revolution

B. Possible Responses
Patriots sided with the American rebels. Loyalists supported the British.

Section 4
A. Possible Responses
1. chose George Washington as military commander; authorized printing of paper money
2. King George rejected the petition and announced new measures to punish the colonies.
3. Americans captured the fort and its cannons and large guns.
4. British won but suffered huge casualties.
5. Continental Army was defeated.
6. Continental Army's show of strength causes British soldiers and Loyalists to leave Boston.

B. Sample Answers
1. Paine's *Common Sense* Urges Colonists to Break Ties with Britain
2. Jefferson Defends Breaking Ties with Britain in *The Declaration of Independence*

The Declaration of Independence

Guided Reading
A. Possible Responses
Purpose—explain to the world the reasons for separating from Britain
Ideas About Rights—Life, liberty, and the pursuit of happiness are rights that can't be taken away. People have the right to overthrow a government that destroys these rights.
Ideas About Government—Governments are set up to protect people's basic rights. People are the government's source of power.
Complaints Against King George III—loss of representative government, quartering of troops without consent, denial of citizenship to recent immigrants, bans on trade with other countries, taxation without representation
B. Responses will vary but ratings should be based on evidence.
C. Possible Responses
[The Right of the People to Control Their Government]—justifies people's right to overthrow a government that denies basic freedoms; spells outs timeless rights of life, liberty, and pursuit of happiness.
[The Colonies Are Declared Free and Independent]—spells out the powers of an independent government.

Building Vocabulary
A. Completion
1. Stamp Act
2. Quartering Act
3. Townshend Acts
4. Intolerable Acts
5. writs of assistance
B. Matching
1. a
2. d
3. j
4. b
5. i
6. g
7. h
8. c
9. f
10. e
C. Writing
Possible Responses
The militia fought bravely against the British.
The colonial boycott of certain products angered the British.

Answer Key

Turn over any Loyalist to the colonial government.
Massachusetts is filled with Patriots.
Minutemen were not as well-equipped as the
British army.

Skillbuilder Practice

Recognizing Propaganda
Possible Responses
1. Americans were unprepared to fight (rifle pointed into the ground, soldier in slouching position, and others scratching their heads and looking confused).
2. The cartoon targets both people and issues. It ridicules American soldiers and pokes fun at their cause of liberty. The caps the American soldiers wear read "DEATH OR LIBERTY"—the reverse of Patrick Henry's cry, "Give me liberty or give me death!"
3. The British might have thought that defeating the colonists would be a simple, easy task.

Geography Application

Section 4: Historic Boston—1775 and Today
Responses may vary on the inferential questions.
Sample responses are given for those.
1. Boston has more than doubled in size, especially when the added land of Charlestown is considered. Boston is barely a peninsula today.
2. the northeastern section, incorporating the areas of Copp's Hill and North Battery
3. Griffin's Wharf seems the most changed. It no longer connects directly to Boston Harbor but is instead completely landlocked.
4. nearly one-half mile
5. Both were primarily connected to the mainland by a thin neck of land.
6. The colonists' fortified position on Breed's Hill overlooked the Boston peninsula. This offered the colonials the possibility of firing canons directly at Boston without risking an immediate encounter with British troops.
7. Their ability to protect Boston from a colonial land assault was great. Because of the water, Americans on ground would find outflanking the British line almost impossible. A direct, risky head-on assault seems the only option.

Primary Sources

Section 1: Resolutions of the Stamp Act Congress
Possible Responses
1. no taxation without representation
2. Only representatives of colonial legislatures have the constitutional right to impose taxes.
3. Resolution XI suggests that colonies might boycott, or be "unable to purchase manufactures [products] of Great Britain."
4. Resolution I proclaims the colonists' loyalty to the "Crown" (or king) and their "subordination" to Parliament.

Section 4: Letter from Abigail Adams
Possible Responses
1. to express concern over the outcome of the battle and to mourn the loss of a friend who died in battle
2. about 24 hours
3. She names the God of Israel and Almighty God. It reflects Adams's deep religious faith.
4. for greater safety and security

Literature Selection

Section 3: "Paul Revere's Ride"
Possible Responses
1. setting—the Old Church and the surrounding areas of Boston in 1775; main characters—Paul Revere and a nameless friend.
2. One lantern will be lit from the belfry if the troops move by land; two lanterns if over water. Revere will wait for the signal and ride through the countryside to alert the sleeping colonists
3. The story in the text tries to explain what happened according to history. The poem dramatizes the events to make them exciting.
4. suggests that future generations will share Paul Revere's patriotic devotion in times of crisis.

Answer Key

Reteaching Activity

Section 1

1. B
2. C
3. C
4. C
5. C
6. C
7. C
8. B
9. B
10. C

Section 2

1. Answer: The Townshend Acts suspended New York's assembly and placed duties on items such as glass, paper, paint, lead, and tea.
2. Question: Why did the colonists protest?
   Answer: The colonists thought that Parliament had violated their rights.
3. Question: How did the colonists protest?
   Answer: They boycotted British goods.
4. Question: What was the Boston Massacre?
   Answer: Some British soldiers fired into a crowd of jeering colonial protesters. Five colonists were killed.
5. Question: Why did the Tea Act upset the colonists?
   Answer: Tea in the colonies could now only be sold by the British East India Company, and colonists would still have to pay a tax on the tea.
6. Question: What was the Boston Tea Party?
   Answer: Colonists, dressed as Native Americans, snuck into Boston Harbor and dumped tea in the harbor to protest the Tea Act.

Section 3

1. King George was furious and vowed to tighten control over the colonies.
2. 1774—Intolerable Acts: (1) closed the port of Boston until colonists paid for the destroyed tea, (2) restricted representative government in Massachusetts, (3) allowed British commanders to house troops wherever necessary, (4) allowed British officials accused of crimes to stand trial in Britain rather than in the colonies.
3. September and October, 1774—The First Continental Congress voted a ban on all trade with Britain until the Intolerable Acts were repealed and called on colonies to begin training soldiers.
4. Parliament had backed down on earlier boycotts, but with the Intolerable Acts, Parliament stood firm.
5. March 1775—Patrick Henry declared that he would rather die than give up liberty.
6. April 18, 1775—Paul Revere and William Dawes alerted the colonists, who took up arms against the British.

Section 4

1. Abigail Adams
2. Ethan Allen
3. George Washington
4. William Howe
5. William Prescott
6. Phyllis Wheatley
7. Benedict Arnold
8. Thomas Paine
9. Thomas Jefferson
10. John Hancock

Answer Key

Setting the Stage

Chart Answers

Possible Responses

1776—British forced Washington from New York. Washington surprised Hessians at Trenton.

1777—Washington won at Princeton. Burgoyne lost at Saratoga. Soldiers suffered at Valley Forge.

1778—France became America's ally. Clark captured Kaskasia. British captured Savannah.

1779—Clark captured Vincennes. Jones defeated *Serapis.*

1780—British captured Charles Town. British defeated Gates at Camden. Americans won at Kings Mountain.

1781—Americans and French forced Cornwallis to surrender at Yorktown.

1783—Americans and British signed Treaty of Paris ending the war.

Discussion Questions

Possible Responses

1. Winter at Valley Forge—hungry, cold soldiers barefoot in the snow
2. 1778; In 1781 French and American forces combined to defeat British at Yorktown.
3. 1778; British victories—Savannah (1778); Charles Town (1780); Camden (1780)

Tracing Themes

Chart Answers

Haym Salomon—refused to collaborate, loaned money

Patriot women—served troops, fought in battles

Thomas Paine—published pamphlets to support cause

Valley Forge troops—refused to give in despite hardship

James Forten—remained loyal despite British offers

1. Citizenship merits no personal reward; the true reward citizens might expect is to see their country prosperous and at peace.
2. Patriots were fighting to create a new nation and a better future. Loyalists embraced their British citizenship and felt that British rule was the best thing for the colonies.
3. The idea that citizens should be required to vote is an opinion; the idea that republican government gets its authority from the people is a fact. Although citizenship and voting are important in a republic, democratic principles do not require everyone to vote. Participation should be encouraged rather than forced.

Guided Reading

Section 1

A. Possible Responses

Patriots: high numbers in New England and Virginia; Native Americans who lived near colonists; African Americans who hoped independence would bring equality

Loyalists: high numbers in the South, in New York State, and in cities; Native Americans who feared that Americans would take their land; African Americans who believed British promises of freedom

B. Possible Responses

1. The British won; they won because of superior numbers; the British occupied New York and the Americans retreated.
2. The Americans won; they took the Hessians by surprise; the American army gained needed supplies, Washington's reputation rose, and the army attracted new recruits.
3. The Americans won; they won because St. Leger and Howe failed to help Burgoyne and because the Americans surrounded Burgoyne; because of Saratoga, European nations decided to help America.

Section 2

A. Possible Responses

1. a young French nobleman who commanded an army division, fought in many battles, and persuaded the French king to send troops
2. a German who trained Washington's inexperienced army into a skilled fighting force
3. a frontiersman who led a force against the British at Kaskaskia and Vincennes, securing the frontier for America
4. a sea commander who defeated the British warship, the *Serapis,* inspiring the American navy

B. Possible Responses

ally: a country that agrees to help another country achieve a common goal

privateer: a privately owned ship that a wartime government gives permission to attack an enemy's merchant ships

Section 3

A. Possible Responses

1. The British won; they won because they could use Savannah as a base and because they surrounded the city; the Americans lost 5,000 troops, almost their entire Southern army, the worst defeat of the war.

Answer Key

2. The British won; they won because the Americans were badly equipped and hungry, and because the American general Gates made mistakes; American morale fell even more, and Gates lost his command.
3. The Americans won; they won because they and their French allies trapped Cornwallis on a peninsula; this effectively won the war for America.

B. Possible Responses
Civilians: vicious raids, feuds between neighbors
Soldiers: hunger, lack of supplies, being outnumbered
Guerrilla Fighters: lack of equipment
C. Possible Responses
Lord Cornwallis: British general forced to surrender at the Battle of Yorktown;
pacificist: person opposed to war

Section 4
A. Possible Responses
Advantages: better leadership, foreign aid, knowledge of the land, motivation
B. Possible Responses
Terms of the Treaty:
1. United States was independent,
2. boundaries were Mississippi, Canada, and Florida,
3. United States received right to fish off Canada,
4. Each side would repay debts,
5. British would return enslaved persons they captured,
6. Congress would recommend the return of seized Loyalist property.

Costs of the War: About 25,700 Americans died, 8,200 were wounded, and 1,400 remained missing. About 10,000 British died. The war left the United States with a debt of about $27 million.
Issues After the War: Americans pursued the goal of republicanism, the idea that the people ruled. They called for more religious freedom. Some Americans wanted to end slavery. Americans were left with the question of how to shape their government.

Building Vocabulary

A. Completion
1. Lord Cornwallis
2. Marquis de Lafayette
3. George Washington
4. John Paul Jones
5. James Forten

B. Matching
1. f
2. g
3. h
4. a
5. j
6. i
7. b
8. d
9. c
10. e
C. Answers will vary, but students should use the terms correctly.

Geography Application

Section 3: Cornwallis Is Trapped at Yorktown, 1781
Responses may vary on the inferential questions. Sample responses are given for those.
1. in eastern Virginia on the inner banks of Chesapeake Bay at the mouth of the York River
2. French ships blockaded the Chesapeake Bay that led to Yorktown.
3. combined French and American armies
4. the Americans; the French
5. the Americans
6. the British
7. about two-thirds of a mile
8. a violent rainstorm
9. The end of British presence in America occurred at a place not far from where it began.

Primary Sources

Section 2: from *Private Yankee Doodle*
1. cold weather and a lack of food and clothing
2. British soldiers killed by the American fieldpiece
3. He was dedicated to winning independence for the United States.
4. 1. The British fought the New England forces at the fence; 2. He joined with another unit; 3. His unit marched towards the enemy's right wing; 4. The first shot by the British cut off the thigh bone of a captain; 5. Martin's unit rested under the fences and bushes; 6. He found a wounded captain and helped him to the surgeons; and 7. Martin stayed a while and watched a few amputations.

Answer Key

Section 4: An African-American Petition for Freedom

1. They have petitioned for changes, waited patiently for responses, and had no success.
2. They want the children of slaves to be freed when they reach the age of 21.
3. The people of Massachusetts condemn the British for denying people their freedom. At the same time they allow slave owners to deny slaves their freedom.
4. Both the petition and the Declaration state that people have rights given them that they can never give up or have taken away.

Literature Selection

Section 1: from *Citizen Tom Paine*
Possible Responses
1. It is retreating. Washington wants Paine to write something to inspire the troops.
2. He is changed from the well-groomed aristocrat Paine met in Philadelphia. He seems haggard and skinny, his face drawn. He admits to not knowing what he thought he knew and is happy to shake Paine's hand. Paine feels that he would gladly die for Washington, or kneel down before him.
3. The troops were inexperienced and outnumbered. Many were despondent, especially in the first years. Ideals were important to the troops. They were inspired by a democratic vision and the sense that their cause was just. Washington was also a source of inspiration.
4. Paine's writing was very important, for it helped inspire the men to fight, bringing comfort and renewed energy when they felt beaten, and it also helped explain and justify their cause.

Reteaching Activity

Section 1
1. Haym Salomon
2. George Washington
3. Mary Hays
4. William Howe
5. Thomas Paine
6. John Burgoyne
7. Joseph Brant or Thayendanegea
8. Benedict Arnold
9. Horatio Gates
10. Tadeusz Kosciuszko

Section 2
1. b
2. b
3. a
4. b
5. c
6. c
7. a
8. b

Section 3
1. D, B
2. A, B
3. B, A
4. C, A

Section 4
A. Possible Responses
1. British generals were too confident and made mistakes. George Washington learned from his mistakes and developed a plan to wear down the British.
2. France and Spain helped the United States with loans and military aid.
3. Americans were able to use their knowledge of the land, while the British had difficulties controlling all but the coastal cities.
4. Americans were fighting for their lives, their property, and their liberty.

B.
1. T
2. T
3. T
4. F
5. T
6. F

Answer Key

Setting the Stage

Reading Strategy
Possible Responses
1. States give up Western claims. Congress passes laws to organize the territories.
2. Annapolis Convention is called to discuss problems of commerce.
3. Philadelphia convention is held. Delegates agree to Great Compromise to settle issue of state representation.
4. Three-Fifths Compromise addresses issue of slavery and representation. Congress delays discussion of banning the slave trade.

Discussion Questions
Possible Responses
1. Passing laws to organize the territories, especially the Northwest Ordinance, set a pattern for the orderly growth of the United States.
2. Economic problems relating to the postwar depression triggered Shays's rebellion—a violent uprising of Massachusetts farmers who were in debt.
3. Great Compromise—legislature with two houses: Senate (equal representation of each state); House of Representatives (representation according to state populations). Three-Fifths Compromise—ratio used to determine representation in the legislature.

Tracing Themes

Diagram Answers
Articles of Confederation—weak national government, strong states
Democratic Principles Shared—republican government, weaker division of power between national and state governments
Constitution—stronger national government, division of power between national and state governments
1. Articles emphasized state and local power to keep the national government from becoming too strong.
2. Small, less-populated states wanted equal representation in Congress, while larger states wanted proportional representation. The solution was to have two houses: one with a proportional basis and the other with equal representation. Students may say that this was a good solution, since it balanced the two positions, though it also produced a more complicated legislative process.
3. Yes—based on the hope of creating a stable governing system that could later provide for basic rights. No—guarantee of people's basic rights too important.

Guided Reading

Section 1
1. There were rich river valleys and large numbers of buffaloes. There were also a few Native Americans who lived, hunted, and fished in the area.
2. Some states refused to accept the Articles until states with Western land claims agreed to give up those claims. By 1781, all of the states agreed that Congress should control the Western lands, and all the states agreed to the Articles.
3. It organized the Northwest Territory geographically into six-mile-square plots, called townships.
4. The legislature did not pass debt relief, which would have helped the farmers. In response, the farmers rebelled.
5. The Northwest Ordinance organized the Northwest Territory politically, instead of geographically. It set rules for the settlement and government of the territories.

Section 2
A. Possible Responses
Characteristics—Well-educated, politically active men; many were heroes of the Revolutionary War; all were wealthy, white men
Generalizations—The Founders were leaders in the nation and they represented the views of rich, white men.
B. Possible Responses
1. two houses with representation according to population or wealth
2. one house with each state having equal votes
3. large states
4. small states
5. It created a two-house legislature with representation by population in one house and equal represention for each state in the other house.
C. Possible Response
Southerners, who represented large numbers of slaveholders, wanted slaves to be counted for population but not for taxation. Northerners, who represented areas where there were fewer slaves, wanted slaves to be counted for taxation but not for representation. The Three-Fifths Compromise settled the issue by counting three-fifths of the slave population for both representation and taxation.

Section 3
A. Possible Responses
1. The Federalists were people who supported ratification of the Constitution.
2. The Antifederalists were people who opposed ratification of the Constitution.

Answer Key

3. Alexander Hamilton, James Madison, and John Jay
4. George Mason and Patrick Henry
5. The Federalists supported removing some powers from the states and giving more powers to the national government. They supported dividing powers among different branches of the government. They also proposed to have a single person lead the executive branch.
6. The Antifederalists wanted important political powers to remain with the states. They wanted the legislature to have more power than the executive. They feared that a strong executive might become a tyrant, and they demanded a bill of rights be added to the Constitution to protect people's rights.

B. Possible Response

A bill of rights was needed because the Constitution did explicitly protect people's rights. It also did not clearly limit the power of the government to keep it from violating people's rights.

Building Vocabulary

A. Completion
1. Shays's Rebellion
2. James Madison
3. republic
4. federalism
5. Bill of Rights

B. Matching
1. d
2. a
3. i
4. f
5. j
6. b
7. g
8. e
9. c
10. h

C. Writing

Possible Response: Under the Articles of Confederation the central government was too weak to act effectively. So, at the Constitutional Convention in 1787, the delegates wrote a new Constitution. Among their leaders was James Madison. Supporters of the stronger central government were called Federalists. Opponents were called Antifederalists.

Skillbuilder Practice

Analyzing Points of View
1. Pendleton likes the phrase because he thinks all power comes from the people.
2. Pendleton thinks that the people are the ones that make decisions, not states.
3. Pendleton supported it.

Geography Application

Section 3: Ratifying the Constitution
Responses may vary on the inferential questions. Sample responses are given for those.
1. Delaware, Georgia, and New Jersey
2. None of the rest of Georgia had returns. This means that no one who lived in that region (mostly Native Americans or Spanish settlers) could vote. Everyone who voted favored the Federalist position.
3. the Federalist position
4. inland, in the more rural or recently developed region
5. Though larger in area, the Antifederalist area was far less populated than the Federalist one.
6. Rhode Island so opposed the Federalist idea of a national government that it did not send representatives to the Constitutional Convention.
7. The United States would have been separated into two regions. New England would have not been connected to the rest of the country by land.

Primary Sources

Section 1: A Letter from Benjamin Lincoln
1. He says that the ease of getting property, credit, and debt have made the people work too little and spend too much.
2. He says the debtors want to overturn the government.
3. Possible Response: He believes the men of property should take the field against the rebels and uphold the government.
4. Because he believes that the U.S. government would be well adminstered, Franklin believes that the new Constitution, even with its faults, should be adopted.

Answer Key

Section 2: from *Debates on the Adoption of the Federal Constitution*

1. He supports it, even though he does not agree with all of it.
2. He wants them to sign the document.
3. Franklin is using humor to remind people that no one is always correct.
4. Franklin is optimistic that the Constitution will be a success because any government will work if people run it well.

Literature Selection

Section 2: from *Our Independence and the Constitution*

Possible answers

1. They allow the states each to behave like a separate country instead of sticking together for mutual protection, political harmony, and more effective government.
2. She is an American girl and feels no loyalty to or nostalgia for the former king. She can barely remember him.
3. Jealousy among the states could lead to their becoming separate countries. Then they might fight each other as European nations do.
4. Because the government can't raise taxes, it can't pay its employees—like Debby's father—a salary that is worth anything. In fact, money has so little value that most people can't afford to buy what they need. So they have to grow or raise their own food and wool.

Reteaching Activity

Section 1

1. F; In the late 1700s, the main road into Kentucky was called the Wilderness Road.
2. T
3. F; The Articles of Confederation gave the state governments the power to set taxes and enforce the law.
4. T
5. F; The Northwest Ordinance described how the Northwest Territory was to be governed.
6. T
7. T

Section 2

1. Philadelphia
2. George Washington
3. Virginia
4. executive
5. New Jersey
6. Great
7. Senate
8. slaves
9. Three-Fifths
10. slave trade
11. Constitution
12. ratification

Section 3

A.

1. F
2. A
3. F
4. F
5. A

B.

1. 2	5. 6
2. 1	6. 7
3. 3	7. 8
4. 5	8. 4

Answer Key

Constitution Handbook

Guided Reading

Preamble and Article 1
A. Possible Responses
1. create a nation in which states cooperate
2. make just laws and set up fair courts
3. maintain peace within the country
4. protect the country against attack
5. contribute to the happiness and well-being of all people
6. make sure all citizens remain free

B. Possible Responses
1. House—at least age 25; lives in state in which elected; U.S. citizen for 7 years. Senate—at least age 30; U.S. citizen for 9 years; lives in state in which elected.
2. House—2 years; Senate—6 years
3. House—varies according to state population; Senate—2
4. House—sole power of impeachment. Senate—power to try impeachment cases
5. House—originates bills for raising money Senate—can make changes in such bills
6. House and Senate jointly can declare war, raise and support armies, provide and maintain a navy.
7. House—none; Senate—acts as president of the Senate

Articles 2 and 3
A. Possible Responses
1. acts as commander-in-chief of the armed forces and militia
2. makes treaties with two-thirds approval of Senate; receives representatives from foreign countries with Senate approval
3. appoints ambassadors, Supreme Court judges, and other important public officials with Senate approval
4. enforces laws passed by Congress; gives annual State of the Union address to Congress; on extraordinary occasions, can call together houses of Congress

B. Possible Responses
1. Supreme Court and other inferior courts set up by the federal government.
2. Supreme Court judges serve for life.
3. Judicial power gives the Supreme Court and other federal courts the authority to hear certain kinds of cases, such as those involving the Constitution, national laws, treaties, and states' conflicts.
4. Judicial review gives the Supreme court the power to declare acts of Congress unconstitutional.
5. Treason is defined as starting a war against the United States or giving aid to its enemies. The testimony of two witnesses or the accused person's confession in court is required for conviction.

Articles 4–7
A. Possible Responses
1. Constitution guarantees each state protection against domestic violence; president can order forces to maintain order.
2. The person must be returned to the first state upon that state's demand.

B. Possible Responses
1. two-thirds of each house of Congress convention, or by a convention called by 2/3 or the state legislatures
2. three-fourths of the state legislatures, or by 3/4 of special conventions held in each state

C.
1. the Constitution
2. federal laws
3. all treaties

D.
1. 9
2. September 17, 1787

Answer Key

The Amendments
Possible Responses

Personal Freedom
Amendment 1 guarantees freedom of press, speech, religion, assembly, and petition.

Amendment 2 guarantees citizens' right to bear arms and form a militia.

Amendment 3 guarantees soldiers cannot be stationed in a private home during peacetime without the owner's consent.

Amendment 4 guarantees citizens' right to privacy for themselves, their homes, and personal property; no unjustified searches or seizures can take place.

Fair Legal Treatment
Amendment 5 protects the rights of people accused of crimes.

Amendment 6 guarantees that people accused of crimes have a speedy, public trial and the right to be represented by a lawyer.

Amendment 7 guarantees citizens' right to a jury trial in a civil case.

Amendment 8 guarantees citizens' right against excessive bail, and cruel and unusual punishment.

Reserved Powers
Amendment 9 guarantees that citizens have rights not explicitly mentioned in the Constitution.

Amendment 10 provides that powers not spelled out in the Constitution belong to states or people.

Election Procedures and Conditions of Office
Amendment 12 requires separate electoral ballots for president and vice-president.

Amendment 17 establishes direct election of U.S. senators.

Amendment 20 changes date for starting new Congress and inaugurating new president.

Amendment 22 limits terms presidents can serve to two.

Amendment 25 sets procedures for presidential succession.

Amendment 27 limits ability of Congress to increase its pay.

Social and Economic Changes
Amendment 11 protects state from lawsuits filed by citizens of other states or countries.

Amendment 13 bans slavery.

Amendment 14 defines citizenship and expands citizens' rights.

Amendment 16 allows Congress to tax incomes.

Amendment 18 prohibits making, selling, and shipping alcoholic beverages.

Amendment 21 repeals Amendment 18.

Voting Rights
Amendment 15 prohibits denying voting rights because of race.

Amendment 19 extends the right to vote to women.

Amendment 23 gives citizens of Washington, D.C., right to vote in presidential elections.

Amendment 24 bans poll taxes.

Amendment 26 gives 18-year-old citizens right to vote.